MP 6310

Chinese proverb
I hear, and I forget
I see, and I remember
I do, and I understand

I do, and I understand

This first published volume of the
Nuffield Mathematics Project is dedicated with gratitude
(and permission) to Jean Piaget

Nuffield Mathematics Project

Published for the Nuffield Foundation
by W & R Chambers and John Murray

Foreword

The last few years have been exciting ones for teachers of mathematics ; and for those of us who are amateurs in the subject but have a taste for it which was not wholly dulled by the old methods that are so often stigmatised, there has been abundant interest in seeing the new mathematical approach develop into one of the finest elements in the movement towards new curricula.

This is a crucial subject ; and, since a child's first years of work at it may powerfully affect his attitude to more advanced mathematics, the age range 5 to 13 is one which needs special attention. The Trustees of the Nuffield Foundation were glad in 1964 to build on the forward-looking ideas of many people and to set up the Nuffield Mathematics Project ; they were also fortunate to secure Dr. Geoffrey Matthews and other talented and imaginative teachers for the development team. The ideas of this team have helped in the growth of much lively activity, throughout the country, in new mathematical teaching for children : the Schools Council, the Local Education Authority pilot areas, and many individual teachers and administrators have made a vital contribution to this work, and the Trustees are very grateful for so much readiness to co-operate with the Foundation. The fruits of co-operation are in the books that follow ; and many a teacher will enter the classroom with a lively enthusiasm for trying out what is proposed in these pages.

Brian Young
Director of the Nuffield Foundation

© The Nuffield Foundation 1967

550 77001 1 (Chambers) Manresa House.
7195 1754 0 (Murray)

First published May 1967
Fifth impression October 1968

Printed in Great Britain by
Newgate Press Limited
London EC1

Contents

1 The need for change

1 The tradition of Victorian arithmetic

Universal elementary education became a reality in this country towards the end of the nineteenth century. The industrial revolution had changed the economic and social patterns to such an extent that it was essential for the rising generation to become literate and to a certain extent competent with figures. The elementary school system was largely designed with this aim in view.

The Victorian clerk, sitting on a stool in a counting house, kept his ledgers meticulously. He wrote in beautiful copperplate, his immaculate figures were neatly underlined, and his calculations were always accurate. Failure in any of these respects would mean the loss of his job. Elementary school education as it then existed encouraged the growth of these skills.

In the twentieth century the pace of life began to quicken. Meticulous presentation and accurate computation were no longer sufficient. Speed was also needed. Until comparatively recently these three considerations predominated in the teaching of primary school arithmetic —

1. meticulous presentation
2. accurate computation
3. speed

2 The age of automation

Less than a century after the introduction of compulsory elementary education the industrial revolution is reaching a climax in the age of automation. Computers can perform even complex calculations at lightning speed: simple calculating machines are available to cope with the everyday computation of business.

There will be less need for people who can perform computations speedily and accurately, and more need for people who can assess situations, who can formulate and solve problems.

3 The changing nature of mathematics

Mathematics itself is changing both to meet the needs of today and to make possible the developments of tomorrow. New ideas have emerged which help to unify aspects of the subject which formerly seemed unrelated to each other. At the frontiers of knowledge, modern mathematics has made the space programme possible. It may be that some of these ideas will prove to be of value in the work of the primary school.

For many years the teaching of traditional arithmetic was kept in its place, one period a day, very frequently timetabled in the first half of the morning. It may be that the time is now ripe for the emancipation of arithmetic, for it to take its rightful place in the wider field of mathematics. It may even be that mathematics itself should be given a roving commission within the new world of primary education.

2 The approach to mathematics in the primary school

1 Why do mathematics?
2 Mathematics and science
3 Mathematics and logic
4 Mathematics and language
5 Attitudes towards mathematics

1 Why do mathematics?

In order to assess the suitability of mathematics for inclusion in the primary school curriculum some consideration must be given to its nature. If mathematics only dealt with abstractions represented by symbols then it would be difficult if not impossible to justify its inclusion in the programme of a primary school.

One dictionary defines mathematics as 'the science of magnitude and number and all their relations'. There is a slightly familiar ring to this. Traditionally it has been accepted that mathematical work with young children concerned number and quantity, that later on it involved the four rules of arithmetic, and their application to common weights and measures. It is in the consideration of 'all their relations' however that the real nature of mathematics becomes apparent.

In the investigation of such relationships patterns emerge, at first sufficient in themselves, and then seemingly inter-related. The recognition of patterns within relationships in itself seems to indicate an aesthetic quality in mathematics, something that very few children formerly had the opportunity to appreciate. Many people can appreciate the elegance of a gracious building, yet few have been enabled to discover a similar elegance in the underlying mathematical patterns and relationships which made such a building possible.

Mathematics offers a way of ordering all experience, pre-school experience, and out of school experience as well as the experience gained from the opportunities offered during the school day. The justification for including mathematics in the curriculum of the primary school would seem to lie in this notion of pattern and relationships, for this is how mathematics has enabled man to discover something of the shape and pattern of the universe, and so move towards the gradual mastery of his environment.

2 Mathematics and science

There are various ways of looking at the approach to mathematics in primary schools and it would be difficult to avoid the conclusion that it is akin to that of science. When a child first meets a new material he experiments with it. This experimentation leads to some hypothesis being formed concerning the material, and at this stage he is rather more concerned with what it *does* and how it does than with what it *is*. Working towards a discovery concerning the nature of the material itself is a more sophisticated approach and typical of a later stage of development.

Having formed a preliminary hypothesis concerning the possible behaviour of this material, he sets about testing his hypothesis. He wants to find out whether it will, for example –
fit into this container
form a parallelogram
weigh about the same as a pint milk bottle
or whatever his hypothesis was. In each case the hypothesis was formed during the preliminary period of investigation. If the hypothesis was shown to be false then the child returns to the material and a further period of free experimentation follows. If his hypothesis was substantiated, if the material did fit into the container (or whatever was suggested) then in many cases there is an urge to communicate. This communication may take many forms. With young children they simply need to tell somebody. Older children will make some kind of written record of their experiment and their findings.

This empirical approach is the natural approach of a primary school child to his environment. It might be summarised as follows:

a. free experimentation with material
b. the formation of a hypothesis
c. the testing of the hypothesis
d. the communication of findings.

3 Mathematics and logic

In later stages of development mathematics and logic appear sometimes to be indivisible. How far can this be said to be true at the primary stage? Certainly the empirical approach described above entails the use of what is called 'inductive reasoning'. Problems are solved on the basis of experimentation, frequently with concrete materials. Deductive reasoning on the other hand involves the making of inferences from given premises. These given premises are not concrete materials but assumptions. This 'deductive reasoning' requires the use of such connectives as

if . . . . then

'*If* I jump into the water *then* I shall get wet'.
This is a logical statement concerning a possible situation.

In the use of *if* and *because* in these statements lies deductive reasoning in embryonic form.

All thought processes are seed beds for the growth of logic, and all practical investigation leads to thinking. Fostering the development of children's thinking implies fostering the growth of logic.

4 Mathematics and language

When communication is considered, mathematics appears as another aspect of language. The first communication takes the form of telling somebody. In this instance normal everyday language as used by a child in his ordinary speech serves the purpose; gradually a wider vocabulary is needed in order to communicate adequately. When the child wishes or needs to record his findings then at first he again uses words. Later he will find the need for symbols other than words in order to clarify his record. These symbols are then seen as a shorthand way of making a record, or another form of what he already knows as language. Pictorial representation in the form of an illustration, a diagram, or a graph also appears as a suitable and convenient way of communicating an experience.

This recording of an experience is an early stage in the use of mathematics as a language. Later the child will need to record the relationships he has perceived within his varied experiences. In the recording of these relationships something of the pattern within mathematics will begin to emerge. Mathematics appears as a language when a child
1. records his experiences   and
2. expresses the perceived relationships within the experiences.

5 Attitudes towards mathematics

$$\text{Experimentation} \rightarrow \text{Thinking} \rightarrow \text{Communication} \begin{cases} \text{by word of mouth} \\ \text{in writing, with words or symbols} \\ \text{by diagram} \end{cases}$$

This seems to be an obvious line of development for a child learning mathematics in a primary school, yet in the discussion on the approach to mathematics the most vital factor has been left until now – does the child *enjoy* and *succeed* in his work? It is recognised that attitudes towards mathematics are largely formed in the primary school and most probably in the first few years. In order to prevent the continuation of certain attitudes prevalent today which manifest themselves in such remarks as

'I was never any good at maths'
'I hated arithmetic'
'Maths always terrified me'
care must be taken to prevent the possibility of their early establishment.

The first remark denotes a sense of failure, the second describes an active dislike, and the third indicates genuine fear. In all probability these attitudes were established for the same basic reason. These children simply did not understand either the work they were required to do or what, in fact, mathematics was all about.

A child's attitude towards a subject is formed in a variety of ways, but the following principles will help to ensure a good one towards mathematics:

1. At all times and at all levels children should have a real understanding both of the problem involved and the possible ways in which it might be approached.

2. Means should be found to enable children to gain some insight into the nature of the subject – that it is forged for man's purpose and therefore variable and that it is an imaginative and creative subject and therefore fascinating.

A group of three discussing their work with their teacher

3 How children learn

1a Learning and teaching

Just how do children learn? There are numerous theories concerning the various aspects of learning. All these are based on research, sometimes with animals, sometimes with children or even adults. Sometimes observations have been made of children or animals in natural situations. Other research has been carried out with individual children or with animals in specially contrived situations. All of it has helped towards the understanding of certain aspects of the learning process, but none of it can fully answer the question 'How do children learn?'.

There is clearly a relationship between learning and teaching, though much learning takes place without any teaching. Conversely there can be teaching that does not lead to learning. The relationship is sometimes obscure. The idea of a 'teacher' tends to complicate the situation; it could be taken to imply that the teacher knows and the child does not know, and so it is the task of the teacher to tell or otherwise instruct him. Today it is recognised that a teacher has not so much a set task to perform as a role to play. An interpretation of this role will be outlined in later chapters.

When teaching is seen as instruction then it is clear that it is the teacher who selects the topic (say long multiplication), demonstrates the process in technique, possibly on a blackboard, and endeavours to explain the topic as he goes along, stage by stage. The art of teaching in this context is dependent upon the use of the imagination in approaching the topic, the careful step by step development, and the skill used in explanation. Many teachers are remarkably skilled in this field, yet none of them would claim complete success. There are always some children who do not seem to understand or cannot grasp the issues involved or, having seemingly understood, cannot apply their new-found skill and knowledge.

1b Memory and practice

Very frequently children are asked to 'remember' such things as number facts or computational techniques. Some remarkable feats of memory have indeed been noted among primary school children. Yet some children find it astonishingly difficult to remember certain things. It is undeniable that some children leave school without being absolutely certain of their multiplication tables, and this in spite of all the efforts of the teacher – praise, encouragement, or threat; cajolery, reward, or punishment have each failed to produce the desired result.

Memory, although a useful tool, is clearly fickle. It seems to operate at different levels, and with different degrees of permanence. It is possible to remember a shopping list, a series of facts for an examination. When the shopping is done, the examination is completed, it is likely that the memory will cease to hold those particular facts. It would seem probable that sustained memory is closely linked with understanding, and that understanding indicates absorption into the existing framework already built in the child's mind. When teaching is seen as instruction then it will be necessary for children to be given the opportunity of practising their new skill. Children are sometimes asked to work twenty pieces of computation of a kind directly related to the example used for the demonstration/explanation part of the lesson. Undoubtedly, practice is necessary, but there is a significant difference between practice that is mere repetition, and practice that reinforces a conceptual experience. Demonstration→explanation→memory→practice can be a successful way of teaching a new skill, but to be valuable the skill must be both useful and used. Unfortunately children quite frequently fail to notice probable applications of the skill. When faced with a problem they might ask 'How do you do it?' or 'Is it a long multiplication?' It seems probable that practice should be seen as the reinforcing of something recently absorbed into the conceptual framework.

2   The contribution of Piaget

Recent work in the field of developmental psychology has thrown light on certain aspects of intellectual growth and development. Although there is valuable research going on in many parts of the world, it is the contribution of Jean Piaget and what is called the Geneva School of Psychology which will be mentioned here.

Piaget describes his method of research as 'clinical'. Test situations and materials have been devised to determine the stages in the building up of the basic frameworks of thought, described as 'mental structures'. The situations are play situations, and throughout the research clear instructions are available to enable testers to deal with any kind of response, in word or action, that the child might give.

This work in Geneva and elsewhere has indicated that although these 'mental structures' are built up gradually there seem to be certain stages through which all children pass.

Several stages are enumerated, but only two will be mentioned here:
1. The stage of intuitive thinking
2. The stage of concrete operations

The research indicates that children of about five years of age – the age when they enter school in Britain – are probably still thinking intuitively, that things are what they *seem* not what they *are*. If a thing *seems* bigger it *is* bigger.

Psychologists working in quite different fields have described what they call the borderline between fantasy and reality, and speak of the slow growth of the fantasy/reality adjustment. The Geneva research has shown the slow growth, and the many interim stages that exist, as the child passes from the stage of intuitive thinking to the stage of concrete operations.

Through a wealth of different experiences the child is enabled to establish the 'invariance' of such things as number,

substance or liquid. He will realise that however he arranges his collection of five pebbles there will still be five. The 'invariance of five' is established. An amount of liquid poured into containers of differing shapes certainly appears to change, but eventually the child will realise that the amount actually remains the same. 'Invariance' of liquid has been established. Once invariance has been established the child is in a position to approach, with confidence, any real problem that arises from the use of concrete materials. The majority of children seem to enter this stage of *concrete operations* at approximately the age of seven.

This stage extends over many years and it seems that the ability to discard all real materials and work abstractly only emerges at around the age of eleven or twelve. There is, however, no spectacular overnight change in approach but a sequence of interim stages.

For example, some children of nine and ten years were investigating the volume of certain containers. They approached the problem in several different ways, one of which was to fill hollow home-made inch cubes with sand and pour them into the containers. After much filling, pouring and counting they declared 'We needn't do this any more. All we have to do is multiply the dimensions'.

Such a moment of enlightenment does not indicate that from then onwards the child will be able to cope with 'formal operations' (the term Piaget uses for the abstract solution of problems) but that he is entering the significant transitional stage. Any attempt to hurry children through this stage of development is liable to lead to a serious loss of confidence. They will discard real materials themselves at the appropriate moment, as the above example indicates, and eventually, when faced with a problem, will ignore all available materials and approach it abstractly.

4 The significance of language

1 The early growth of language

The essence of communication is language, whether in the spoken or written form. There is a certain degree of social conformity involved, for the child learns to speak and use the language of his parents and the community in which he lives. Language begins with babbling and gurgling sounds which are gradually refined into acceptable speech patterns. This process is wholly dependent upon the sense of hearing, and a child who never hears spoken language will not naturally learn to speak.

In the early stages speech is largely imitative, and occurs within the framework of the mother/child relationship. The mother says something and the child attempts to imitate the sound pattern.

Later the adult will be beset by questions from the early 'What's that?' to the later 'Why?'. In answering the question 'What's that?' the adult is helping the child to name some specific object in his immediate environment. Once the object has a name it will assume a new significance for the child. In answering the question 'Why?' the adult is fostering the growth of the idea of causation, and the beginning of reasoning.

Research in England in this field seems to indicate that this is a vital stage of growth, and that there is a significant relationship between the quality of the language heard, and therefore used by the child, and his present and future intellectual development.

Three factors seem to determine the quality of the experience in these vital pre-school years:
1. The quality of play opportunity in terms of space, time and materials.
2. The availability of a companion, and particularly an understanding adult with whom to talk.
3. The quality of the language used.

2 Language growth at school

Some young children arrive at school with a considerable command over language. They have a wide-ranging vocabulary and surprising powers of description. Others are barely articulate and have great difficulty with any kind of communication. These varied starting points are dependent upon the quality of the child's pre-school experience. The role of the teacher is to determine the starting point, and to provide the opportunities necessary for language growth to meet the needs of each child.

Language does not grow in a vacuum but in relationship to real materials and situations. Imaginative play at this stage is primarily imitative, and here the observant teacher becomes aware of the speech patterns of the child's home environment. Opportunities for the teacher actively to foster language growth arise in creative play when the child is experimenting with new materials. New materials present an exciting challenge to children, who need at first to experiment quite freely, with no direction or even suggestion from the teacher.

This stage of experimentation can sometimes last for a considerable period, but the time comes when the children feel the urge to communicate. They need to tell somebody. Sometimes words come spilling out to fulfil this desire to communicate, but sometimes they get stuck for lack of an adequate vocabulary. Here the role of the teacher is quite clear. He must so infiltrate the necessary vocabulary into his responses that the child hears these words in the context of an enjoyable experience.

3 Discussion

The understanding of what is meant by discussion in the primary school is intricately bound up with an appreciation of classroom relationships. The primary school teacher has the inestimable advantage of really knowing the children in his care, for in all probability they will spend most of the school day together. When authoritarianism prevailed, such discussion as existed almost inevitably took the form of question and answer — the teacher asking the question and the children supplying the answers. There is obviously still a place for this kind of activity in certain circumstances, but it does not constitute what is today recognised as discussion. In any event it must be acknowledged that, although the children who supplied the answers gained a degree of self-satisfaction from the activity, there were always children who suffered acute embarrassment.

In the more permissive atmosphere that prevails in primary schools today it is acknowledged that if children are to have opportunities for all-round development, social and emotional as well as intellectual, then they must have real contact with each other through speech. The role of the teacher today is not to stop children talking but rather to ensure that there is something very worthwhile for them to talk about. In this kind of atmosphere there is a place for lively class discussion, and the quality of the discussion will be directly dependent upon the quality of the teacher/class relationship. It has to be accepted that every person in the room has something to offer and is entitled to hold an opinion. Where mutual trust and tolerance exist, then confidence grows, and confidence plays a considerable part in the growth of fluent speech.

Since classes are large and unlikely to grow noticeably smaller, class discussion will be seen to have certain limitations. If discussion is to foster not only language, but thought and reasoning, then it needs to take place in much smaller groups. Sometimes it will be possible for a discussion to take place between a teacher and an individual child; more often it will be between a teacher and a small group of children. Personal relationships are again significant. A child learns to respect the opinions of others through the respect the teacher shows for his point of view. It is in the context of small group discussion that a teacher can profitably make use of the word *Why?*. When the children confidently reply 'Well — because . . .' then thought and reasoning are clearly being fostered.

The third kind of discussion is that which takes place between child and child. Children frequently gossip or chat. Socially no doubt this kind of talk is valuable but it makes little contribution to intellectual development. However, when class and group discussions play a significant part in the school programme, then there is a noticeable carry-over. Children will be observed and overheard in classroom, playground or street carrying on earnest discussions.

Real discussion, wherever it appears, is provoked by experience. Sometimes a situation arises spontaneously or it may in some way be contrived by the teacher. The situation supplies the starting point; the discussion that ensues should widen the child's horizons and open up many new avenues of exploration.

On the way to school one day some junior children noticed that one of the manhole covers in the street outside the school had been removed. They commented on this to their teacher, and a lively discussion ensued concerning not only the use but the shape and dimensions of these covers. The subsequent investigation involved why things had differing shapes and sizes, for example, the various sizes of school hoops, and also the construction of rectangular frameworks from bamboo canes.

5 Learning through discovery

1 Active learning

From time to time certain words attain a new significance through their use in the vocabulary of educationalists. Quite frequently they are subsequently mis-used and abused or at any rate widely misunderstood. The word 'discovery' stands in danger of such misinterpretation today. In order to understand why it is now widely believed that children learn through their own discoveries, and what, in this context, is meant by 'discovery', it is necessary to consider some of the wider implications.

The Hadow Report of 1931 contained this famous sentence: 'The curriculum is to be thought of in terms of activity and experience rather than knowledge to be acquired or facts to be stored'. In this instance it was the words 'activity' and 'experience' that became emotive, and were widely mis-interpreted. Not that they were inappropriate: rather that the climate of opinion was not yet ready to accept them in the context of the classroom situation. Even then, in 1931, there was nothing very surprising in the statement. Good teachers had always felt instinctively that their children seemed happiest and even seemed to learn most through 'doing'. This report foreshadowed the exciting developments of primary education notably in the post-war years. Teachers have discovered that knowledge can be acquired and facts gradually stored through 'active learning', and that when children are actively involved in real situations the process can be most exciting for teachers as well as children. The work of Piaget would seem to indicate that the majority of the children in primary schools are passing through what he terms the stage of concrete operations, that they are able to deal confidently with real problems arising from the use of concrete materials. The evidence produced by his team of research workers fully substantiates and justifies the belief that children learn through activity and experience.

All experience, and not least that in the realm of mathematics, offers the possibility of the discovery of relationships. A young child will discover that 'this lid fits on to this tin'. There is a relationship between the lid and the tin. Older children measuring their heights and shadows will discover that there is an interesting relationship between them. Children who have been encouraged to look for patterns and relationships within their experiences develop a particular sensitivity. In the early stages of this work it is more than likely that there will be some children who, say, measure heights and shadows, but never look beyond the actual measurements and so discover nothing. It is the role of the teacher to suggest a certain arrangement of the data, or to ask a question demanding some evaluation of the data in order to lead the child to the discovery of the relationship. This demands great skill from the teacher. It is so much easier just to tell the child what to look for, yet the whole joy of discovery is thereby missed.

2 Problems

When primary school mathematics consisted largely of arithmetic and was thought of only in terms of knowledge to be acquired and facts to be stored the subject was frequently sub-divided into 'mental', 'mechanical' and 'problems'. A problem in this context meant a piece of mechanical arithmetic disguised by the use of words. The disguise was all too often quite successful, and children found difficulty in unravelling the words and revealing the mechanical arithmetic. On other occasions the disguise was thin and no 'problem' at all was posed.

But a real problem involves far more than this, for it involves both the objective assessment of a situation and the posing of a question concerning it. Problem-provoking situations can arise or may be teacher-contrived. This will be considered more fully in Chapter 6, 'The use of the environment'.

The solution of genuine problems and the judgement-making involved are integral parts of living. This is particularly true of

A group of three in the classroom discussing among themselves the graph they have made from their findings a democratic society going through an era of rapid change. The confidence to assess situations, formulate questions, and attempt to determine solutions only grows through experience, yet it is something that all children urgently need today. This confidence is intricately bound up with the growth of a healthy attitude towards mathematics without which there can be little progress made.

There remains the whole question of motivation. If a problem is really meaningful to the child then he will be strongly motivated to solve it. It is only when the problem is totally divorced from the 'here and now' of the child's personal interest and experience that the unreality obviates genuine motivation. It is, of course, possible to motivate children by means of a system of rewards. A young child will endeavour to get his sum right in order to gain a tick, the symbol of success and approval. An older child will work hard to solve his equation in order to pass his examination. Both these are artificial motivational devices which have of necessity evolved within a competitive society. If the problem emerges within the framework of the child's experience, then no artificial device is needed to encourage him to work towards a solution.

3 Questions

If a problem involves the posing of a question concerning a particular situation it must be determined who it is who asks the question, and of whom. Formerly it was accepted that it was the teacher who asked the questions in the classroom situation, and the children who supplied the answers. Such questions were almost inevitably 'closed'; there was no real enquiry. The teacher already knew the answer, and posed the question in such a way as to obtain the correct response from the child.

For example: 'What are seven eights?' Correct response: 'Fifty-six'.

It was, of course (and still would be), very important to 'get this right'.

But it is now recognised that there is a place for children's questions as well as those of the teacher, and for 'open-ended' as well as 'closed' questions. There are occasions when there is a particular and precise answer to a problem; in effect the question is 'closed'. Not all problems, however, lead to a solution of this nature. Some situations open up many avenues of investigation, and in the beginning it is by no means certain that one precise answer is possible. Questions arising from these situations are the ones referred to as being 'open-ended'.

Children's questions can arise in many ways. Sometimes an experience in or out of school provokes a direct question posed by an individual child to a teacher. It is all too tempting for the teacher to supply an answer, but the role of the teacher in this circumstance is to discuss the situation with the child. From such discussion a possible avenue of investigation will emerge. One of the most difficult tasks a teacher has to face is to refrain from giving direct answers: the child must be encouraged to make discoveries for himself.

It must be remembered that children's questions arise from varying needs. Sometimes the question is a function of natural curiosity, sometimes it reveals an emotional need. A disturbed child will ask questions simply to gain the attention of the teacher. In recognising this need and meeting it by having a few moments' discussion with the child, the teacher will be making a significant contribution towards his eventual stability.

Questions can arise from an organised group activity. Some 6-year-olds had made a block graph concerning their birthdays. They noticed that the April column was higher than that of any other month. After some discussion a clear question emerged, 'Are there always more people born in April than in any other month?' To the children at first it seemed as if this was a 'closed' question. It could be answered by a 'Yes' or a 'No'. Their subsequent investigations led them to conclude, 'Unless we could ask everyone in the world we couldn't find out'. They had discovered the inadequacy of their original graph: that in statistical terms the size and selection of the sample affects the validity of the conclusions.

Other questions arise from a common experience. One day some men arrived to paint the lines on the school playground, and in particular the lines of the netball court. Some children who had become interested in circles asked 'Are those goal circles on our netball court true semi-circles?' Here again the question appeared to be 'closed' and, in fact, proved to be so. But the lines of investigation initiated by the children not only solved the immediate problem but opened up new fields of enquiry. For example, some children became interested in other shapes actually on the playground.

It was suggested in Chapter 2 that the natural approach of a primary school child to his environment is an empirical one, and that the last stage of an investigation concerned the communication of findings. When children reach a conclusion to their investigation which satisfies them they frequently discuss it with their teacher. It is through this discussion that the teacher can determine just what the child has gained from the experience, and so make some estimate of his progress.

6 The use of the environment

1 The environment

In educational circles today much use is made of the word 'environment'. What do we mean by environment? So often it is interpreted as concerning the measuring of the playground, or a visit to a local museum. It is surely far more than this. It might, perhaps, be interpreted as the people, the places and the things that surround us.

The child is at the centre of an ever-widening world. At first his world consists of himself and his mother. Gradually his world widens to include home and family, street, neighbourhood and school. The world of the research physicist has widened to the extent of the inclusion of outer space. For the primary school child the environment includes
a. the people at home and at school
b. the places he knows well or can easily visit
c. the things he can see, feel, hear and touch.

2 Looking and listening

The very young child instinctively uses his senses in his exploration of the environment. He grasps things and frequently sucks them in an attempt to assess their nature. From *touching* and *tasting* he moves to the position in which he can learn much by *looking* and *listening*. Unfortunately there are many factors in life today that militate against looking and listening to such an extent that the skill is often partly lost. If people saw and heard everything that exists in their immediate environment they would become submerged beneath the welter of sights and sounds. Because of this pressure on the senses people have gradually learned to become selective in their looking and listening. They just do not notice crude glaring posters, ugly buildings and other things loosely described as 'eyesores'. This is an inevitable adaptation of man to his environment.

Those who live and work in busy streets learn to ignore the noise of traffic. At home there may be music from the radio but they need not hear it. Although this form of selective looking and listening makes life in general more tolerable it can have a startling effect on the particular skills involved. Conditions are such that children grow up unable to look closely or listen acutely, and yet these very powers are essential if the environment is to be fully exploited as an educational agency.

As much of the school day is of necessity passed in the classroom the people and things there constitute the most significant part of a school child's environment.

Mathematical activity, as any other classroom activity, can derive from the most commonplace objects if and when powers of observation are developed. Children and teachers need to look at their surroundings with new eyes, to notice the relationships between the dimensions of windows and doors, tables and chairs, cupboards and blackboards, to use the heights, characteristics, habits and interests of children for elementary statistical surveys.

3 The role of the teacher

Initially the role of the teacher is to help the children to acquire acute powers of observation and to assess the possibilities that lie within the most commonplace objects and events. Gradually these possibilities will have been investigated and there will be need for new stimuli. Then the role of the teacher will be to provide interesting materials to stimulate further work. This is sometimes referred to as 'conditioning the environment'. If the teacher feels that the children need experience in the field of volume and capacity then he must so 'condition the environment' as to make this experience possible. This means the provision of containers and materials with which to fill them. The mere provision of materials however is not quite sufficient. The situation must be carefully structured by the teacher if the children are to make real discoveries.

Whenever new materials are introduced there seem to be three separate stages through which children must pass. At first the child needs a period of free experimentation with the material. The duration of this period will depend upon his age and ability and upon his previous experience of the material. The second stage involves the introduction of the necessary vocabulary related to the particular materials. This vocabulary is best introduced through teacher/child discussion while the materials are actually being handled. The third stage sees the emergence of a problem – probably some question that has arisen during the discussion. This sequence
1. free experimentation
2. introduction of vocabulary
3. emergence of a problem,
seems to arise naturally. It is certainly not imposed or even obviously contrived. It is representative of an unobtrusive, yet carefully structured, situation.

One day a new water trolley arrived in an infant classroom. Delighted, the teacher duly filled it with warm water, tied waterproof aprons around the excited children, and produced a set of standard metal containers. "Now, see if you can find out how many times you have to fill up the little container in order to fill the big one." The children set to work with glee and in a few moments produced an answer. "Nine," they said triumphantly.

This was a problem posed by the teacher. In effect she was asking "How many pints are there in a gallon?" But the children were not yet ready for any kind of problem. They had not had the necessary long period of experimentation during which they would have discovered something of the nature of water – that it has to be contained before it can be measured – that certain skills have to be developed and particular tools used in order to transfer it from one container to another. Neither had the necessary vocabulary been introduced. There is much to be discussed about the use of the word 'full' and its meaning in different situations. The children

had not miscounted. They had not been careless. The situation had simply not been structured with sufficient care to make such a question meaningful or profitable.

There is sometimes a little concern among teachers as to the kind of materials to provide, and when to introduce them. To a certain extent it is the personal confidence of the teacher in the mathematical field which provides this situation. However, if at first this environmental work is concentrated upon that which already exists in the classroom it will be possible at some stage for a teacher to assess what kind of experiences have emerged during this period, and what kind of opportunity has been lacking. The first provision of extra materials can then be selected in order to fill one of these noticeable gaps.

4   Beyond the classroom

Education does not take place solely within the four walls of the classroom. Learning takes place in and out of the school building, and in and out of school time. The time comes when teacher and children are ready to venture farther afield in their use of the environment. At first there must be encouragement of real observation outside the classroom. Children will readily collect information at home or on the way to school to support some investigation taking place in school hours.

Later it will seem possible for children to be working outside the classroom in corridor, hall, playground or field actually during school time. It might be possible for a whole class to be involved in some outside activity. More frequently one or two groups might be working outside while the remainder are in the classroom. The success of this arrangement is dependent upon the existing classroom relationships. Where tolerance and trust have been established no problems arise. Children will adopt the same attitude to their work wherever it may be taking place, and whether the teacher is with them or not. They do need to know where the teacher may be found, whether he is inside or out, in case there is a need for urgent consultation.

On many occasions children can be making use of the immediate environment for a specific mathematical purpose. On the other hand, an organised visit may take place for a totally different purpose, perhaps in connection with a local study, yet mathematical possibilities may appear. Incidental opportunities also exist in other circumstances. For example, a group of ten-year-old boys were engaged in some work on flight. One morning two of them were bird-watching in the school field, taking particular note of flight manoeuvres. They went back into school, collected a stop watch, and made some records of the number of wing beats per minute of all the different kinds of birds they could see. Then they compared this data with that obtained from counting the number of footfalls per minute as the fastest runner in the class ran across the field. From this point onwards, there was plenty of mathematics involved.

The aim in all this work must be to cultivate in teachers and children alike an awareness of the possibilities that lie within the environment in order that full use be made of it.

Working in pairs in the playground

7 Problems of organisation within the school

1 Time available
2 People concerned

1 Time available

The curriculum of the one-time 'elementary' school developed in a rather piecemeal fashion, with the gradual introduction of additional 'subjects' as and when it seemed appropriate. As such 'subjects' proliferated it became the task of the head teacher to fit them all in to the daily or weekly programme of the school. Hence the growth of the precise timetable in order to ensure that all children had opportunities within the current range of 'subjects'.

The 1944 Education Act viewed education as a total process moving through several stages. The old elementary school disappeared, and the first few years of a child's education, until the age of eleven or thereabouts, was termed the *Primary* stage.

Concurrently with this administrative change different attitudes towards the curriculum began to emerge. The new emphasis lay on the total learning process rather than on the range and diversity of 'subjects'. There were areas where subject barriers began to crumble and the restrictions of a timetable were keenly felt. Flexibility became the key word. The latest 'subjects' to become involved in this kind of flexible curriculum are science and mathematics. The question that is now being asked is 'If mathematics is to be viewed in this new light, how much time can or should be devoted to it?'

In schools where there is a wide degree of flexibility within the school day, mathematics is already contributing more than was previously thought possible to children's investigations in the field of local studies, project work or the like. Here future development will probably involve a gradual lessening of the separate time devoted to the mastery, and indeed to the continual revision, of computational skills. It will become apparent that much of this work can and does arise in the general context of investigation. Such separate time as is still found necessary for mathematics will probably be devoted to the practice of skills which have arisen and been dealt with during some experiment.

Other schools will have other kinds of problems. In schools where a timetable exists and is to a large extent adhered to, the development will probably be along different lines. In the first instance it would perhaps be wiser to retain the existing structure of the day. Children and teachers frequently need this kind of security. Within the agreed amount of time in the school day the emphasis would then be on the gradual transition from the teaching of arithmetic to children's discoveries in the field of mathematics. As the work progresses it will be seen that there is much language work involved in this kind of approach. It will also be seen that the time allocation which formerly seemed quite adequate seems to fly by when children are pursuing their own investigations. Teachers will readily agree that children should be encouraged to complete a piece of work to their own and their teacher's satisfaction. It can be extremely frustrating both for teachers and children when time after time work on some topic has to be suspended. To meet this difficulty it might be possible to allow a longer stretch of time, recognising that in recording their findings the children are doing a very significant and purposeful piece of written English.

2 People concerned

Not all primary school teachers are completely confident about the teaching of arithmetic, and they are now asked to cope with the wider world of mathematics in which they might have even less confidence. Small wonder that there is not only bewilderment but apprehension. The question here is 'How far is it reasonable to expect a primary school teacher to cope with this new development?'

The answer surely lies in the changing role of the teacher, who is not, today, expected to be the fount of all wisdom and able to answer every question. Children gain great respect for a teacher who can smile and say 'Well, I'm afraid I don't know the answer to that one, but maybe together we can find out'. In this way children and teacher will be learning.

Together they can carry out enquiries, devise experiments, or search for appropriate help from books and other sources.

It is sometimes suggested that a specialist teacher of mathematics might be appointed to a primary school. This might entail the adoption of techniques appropriate to secondary schools; possibly the establishment of a mathematics room in which this specialist taught, with each class having a time-tabled period in the room. Such an approach, however, would seem to contradict all current educational thought and practice in primary schools, and would militate strongly against the further reunification of the artificial man-made subject barrier now recognised as inappropriate for younger children.

The question of the mathematics room will be dealt with in a later chapter. The question of the mathematics specialist is one that merits further discussion here. It is obviously unreasonable to expect every primary teacher to have a particular interest in mathematics. When conditions such as have been described above obtain, with teachers being prepared to go along with the children in the path of discovery, great use could be made of any member of staff who has or is willing to acquire a special interest in this field. He would act not as a specialist but rather as a consultant in cases of difficulty. Children and teachers alike, and in some cases together, could ask for his help in the solution of problems. This is not to say that he would provide the answer; he would probably suggest another, more fruitful, avenue of approach to the problem.

Where the school day is organised for maximum flexibility and movement within the school is encouraged, then it is possible for all members of staff to develop a particular interest or skill, and to share this interest among all the children of the school by acting as a consultant in their own chosen field. Maximum use is then made of the available talent among the staff, to the great benefit of both children and teachers.

8 General problems of class organisation

1 The flexible day

The school day for a primary school child normally begins some time between 9 a.m. and 9.30 a.m. and ends at approximately 4 p.m. This period of time is divided into morning and afternoon sessions, and frequently these sessions are further divided by a ten-or fifteen-minute break. This four-session day is the most usual structural framework within which a teacher plans his work.

In some infant schools and a few junior schools the mid-morning and mid-afternoon breaks have disappeared in order to make possible even greater flexibility and continuity. For many years some infant schools have been working within this framework which is sometimes described as 'an un-differentiated curriculum' or 'a free day'. It is believed that the lack of unnecessary interruption enables children to develop greater powers of concentration and sustained effort, for it is almost always possible for a child to complete a task once he has embarked upon it. This leads to a sense of achievement and even the development of a critical faculty in cases where the child is encouraged to join with the teacher in evaluating his efforts.

The majority of primary schools still function within a clearly defined structural framework although in many instances the declared purpose of the timetable is to act as a rough guide to the teacher, and there is no suggestion that it should be strictly adhered to.

Some degree of flexibility, it seems, is almost universal, and this will make possible further developments in mathematical work in primary schools.

2 Class organisation

It may now be recognised that children learn through active involvement with real situations and real materials, and that discussion plays a vital part in the development of children's thinking. The question for the teacher is how to organise the class to make this 'active learning' possible.

Class work, in the sense of all the children being involved in the same activity at the same time, will be seen to have severe limitations, though there will be occasions when a class discussion is not only desirable but essential. Occasionally an individual child will pose his own problem and, with the help of the teacher, work towards its solution. The most usual pattern of organisation, however, involves some form of grouping.

There is much to be said for allowing children to work in pairs. In this instance conversation develops naturally into a discussion of the problem involved. The unit of two is also useful during the investigation, one child being involved in the operation while his partner records any findings as the work progresses. When the practical side of the work is complete, together they will survey and evaluate the findings and discuss the most suitable way of making a more permanent record of their work: whether, for example, it would be more suitable to make a model, construct a table, or draw a graph.

Sometimes larger groups, of three or even more children, may seem more suitable. There are three possible ways of approaching the problem of dividing a class into groups for this purpose.

a. The mixed ability group
In this group there will be able, average and less able children, each making his own contribution. In particular the able will be helping the less able, and the less able will gain a sense of belonging. Some teachers, however, claim that the able children tend to be understretched in such groups.

Individual work, using a clinometer

b. The common ability group

In this group the children will have similar ability and have reached a similar level of attainment. There will be little possibility of anyone being left behind; rather, the children will spur each other on.

c. The friendship group

In this group children will be working with chosen companions. On analysis, this group frequently contains not only children of similar ability but those sharing similar interests.

It will be for the teacher to decide both the size of the group, and how the groups should be constituted.

3　Possible beginnings

There will be some schools in which mathematics is still arithmetic, still confined within timetable limits, and there will quite naturally be some anxiety among teachers as to how to effect a changeover. In no circumstances should the sense of security among children or teachers be jeopardised. New ideas should be allowed to grow beside the old, until gradually assessment becomes possible and in all probability some of the old will be replaced by new.

The problem for the teacher is how to effect this changeover, bearing these principles in mind. There are as many possible beginnings as there are teachers. The three approaches discussed here have already been found helpful in these circumstances.

a. Friday afternoons

Even in the most formal schools teachers readily admit that there are times in the week when a more relaxed atmosphere prevails. Frequently Friday afternoon is mentioned. Many teachers have made their beginning by introducing a mathematical problem involving exploration of real materials in the context of the informal Friday afternoon.

b. A mathematics table or corner

In some schools a beginning has been made with the introduction of a mathematics corner or table, sometimes sited in a classroom, sometimes in a corridor or the school hall. On the table would be certain attractive and provocative materials and possibly a few cards posing questions concerning the materials. Some schools have instigated competitions centring around these mathematics tables, the children being asked to submit in writing their answer to the questions by a certain time. In assessing the entries teachers have not only looked for correct solutions (where these were possible) but for evidence of children's thinking. No prizes are awarded. The discussions arising from the queries of one week frequently trigger off next week's problem.

c. One group at a time

Both the possible beginnings outlined above have enabled the traditional arithmetic lesson to remain intact for the present. An alternative beginning means that one group each day is involved in practical 'discovery' work while the rest are carrying on with normal routine. By allowing a different group each day this kind of opportunity, every child has a chance of 'discovery' work at least once a week.

Each of these suggested beginnings makes but slight demand on the teacher. Only a small amount of material needs to be assembled when provision is being made for only six or eight children at a time. As interest and enthusiasm grow and more time is devoted to this kind of work so more materials will be needed.

4　Problems that arise

Many years ago children were not allowed to pick up their pencils without permission. Even today there are occasions when teachers say 'Take out your arithmetic books'. It must be accepted that there is a great gulf between the listening-for and acting-on instructions, and the free selection and use of materials. In the interim period, before the children have become self-reliant, teachers will be beset by questions such as 'May I use this yardstick?' and 'Can I get the scales?'.

This means an unnecessary waste of the teacher's time in answering the question, and additional unnecessary movement within the classroom as the child comes to the teacher to ask it. Yet it is an essential stage in the development of this work. It will be grown through gradually as children gain more self-sufficiency and confidence.

Inevitably there will be additional noise at the beginning. Of course the children will be excited about their work. The movement of children around and beyond the classroom, the clamour of voices discussing materials, equipment, possible methods of approach – all this puts an additional, but only temporary, burden on the teacher. The amount of noise and even mischief that arises will be dependent upon
a. the previous classroom conditions
b. the way the changeover has been effected. The more gradually new approaches are introduced the greater the likelihood of eventual and lasting success.

9 Some particular problems of class organisation

1 Rural and urban schools
2 Vertical or horizontal age grouping
3 Streamed or unstreamed classes
4 Problems of immigrant children

1 Rural and urban schools

As each child is unique so is his environment. If mathematics in the primary school is to be derived from and interwoven with the child's environment some attention must be paid to the differences and divergences and the effect these must have on the classroom situation. Comparisons could be made regionally, of the North with the West, the South and the Midlands, and the discussion will certainly involve two broad categories of schools, urban and rural. The speed of life varies enormously according to the environment and this has its effect in the classroom. The rapid pace of life in a city influences city children in that they react more quickly to situations, are likely to accept new ideas more readily and work faster. At the same time they tend to be superficial in much that they attempt. Rural children tend to work and adapt more slowly though they more naturally achieve some depth in their work.

The children of these contrasted communities will have vastly differing pre- and out-of-school environmental experiences. Children brought up in the confined conditions of an over-crowded city have only rare experiences of space and distance, while rural children have a wealth of such experience. City children have every opportunity to help them towards the eventual understanding of large numbers and quantities. They are familiar with the congestion of a city street. Hundreds of children play in the school playgrounds; thousands take part in the Area Sports Festival. For a rural child the only place where he might see a thousand or more of anything would be leaves on a tree or blades of grass in a field.

In making provision for children's needs account should therefore be taken of the unique environment of the particular school. Full advantage should be taken of any local peculiarities; for example, much interesting work on shapes was done in a school completely surrounded by a large bomb-site. On the other hand, experiences which are not readily to hand can be made available by 'structuring' the situation. For example, the rural child might take part in a project to assemble a million square inches of graph paper ('do you think they would completely cover this wall?'); the town children could perhaps do some elementary 'judging distance' in the local park.

2 Vertical or horizontal age grouping

It is the task of the head teacher to share the available teachers among the children of the school. In large schools horizontal age grouping is most commonly used, the children in any class all being of a similar age, sometimes within a span of a year, sometimes with as little as a six-month range.

Rural schools have never been in a position to make this decision for they have rarely had sufficient children on roll to justify a teacher for each age group. The extreme case of this situation is the now rare and fast disappearing one-teacher school, where the teacher was responsible for all the children between 5 and 11 years of age. Still quite common is the two-teacher school with one teacher responsible for the 5 to 7 age range and the other for the 7 to 11. Most common of all in country areas is the three-teacher school, the children being distributed in age groups as follows: 5 to 7, 7 to 9, 9 to 11. This is *vertical* age grouping made necessary by local conditions. There has, however, been an increasing tendency of late to employ this method of grouping children by choice, notably in infant schools. A large school may have as many as ten parallel classes, each catering for the full 5 to 7 age range. The name *family grouping* or *all-age* grouping is sometimes used in this context.

It is felt by many people that it is easier for one teacher to plan for forty-five 8-year-olds than for another who has forty-five 7- to 9-year-old children. This was undoubtedly true when the mathematics work was confined to the teaching of arithmetical skills. Today it will be agreed that these two teachers face completely different problems of classroom organisation but viewpoints will vary as to which is the easier situation.

The planning for the horizontally-grouped class should take the following factors into account:

a. Being of a similar age the children are likely to have similar interests.

b. They will have had similar school experiences in the preceding years.

c. They will in all probability have been together as a unit for some time, moving up the school year by year.

d. It is unlikely that they will have had the same teacher for more than one year.

e. Even if they are unaccustomed to working in groups in the classroom friendship groups will have emerged in the playground.

The teacher has the great advantage that although at first he doesn't know them they all know each other quite well. Group work should not be difficult to arrange. On the other hand, the provision of suitable materials will pose greater problems.

When a certain selection of materials appears in the classroom children have been known to make such remarks as "We had that last year" or "We've done that". It will be seen therefore that the role of the teacher is not only to *extend* the range of materials, but to help the children to discover further possible avenues of investigation using *familiar* materials. A wide range of experiences will have to be contrived within these given limits, taking into account the common experiences the children had in the previous class and the range of their current interests.

Planning for the vertically-grouped class will be based upon different factors, and can be far more flexible. The continuity of work can be easily maintained as the teacher never faces an entirely strange class. Approximately two-thirds of the children are in the same classes as they were last year.

In a class with a wide age-range quite frequently one starting point will serve as a springboard for investigations at different levels, each of which illuminates or enhances the others. For example, a selection of tins (with lids) acquired from a chemist provided a very wide range of opportunity for a group of children between 5 and 8 years old. The 5-year-olds matched lids to appropriate tins, and attempted to arrange both lids and tins in order of size. The 8-year-olds investigated the dimensions and volumes of the tins.

With careful handling older children can gain considerable insight into the difficulties of those who are younger than they are. They will learn how to frame a question that will enable a younger child to make a discovery, and will share his sense of achievement. When the teacher intends a certain provision to be just for the older children of the group it is sometimes impossible to prevent the younger ones from joining in. In these circumstances they may make quite unpredictable strides in achievement or they may just experience a great sense of wonder at the activities of the older ones.

3   Streamed or unstreamed classes

The disadvantages of the horizontal age group as outlined above are intensified by streaming. The range of ability, achievement and interest is narrowed still further, and the task of the teacher to provide a diversity of challenging materials and situations is made still more difficult.

Where streaming is employed in school organisation it is usually geared to some kind of objective assessment, generally in the form of an attainment test. These children will be accustomed to the kind of competition which leads to a form of value judgement based on 'How many marks did you get?'. All children enjoy a degree of competition, but this over-emphasis on the competitive element has had a profound effect on the teaching of arithmetic, particularly in streamed schools. The marks obtained in arithmetic have, in fact, played a major part in determining the 'stream' in which the child was placed.

The introduction of 'discovery methods' will help a child to see that while sometimes there is value in *competing against* other children there is greater value in *co-operating with* them. It is possible for a teacher to so organise his work in mathematics that children begin to experience a new kind of value judgement, based on the assessment of situations, the formation and solution of problems, the degree of co-operation within the group. If this aim is accepted then the introduction of discovery work in mathematics offers a most exciting challenge to the teacher of a streamed class. So-called 'A' children might learn more humility, 'C' children gain a new sense of achievement.

4   Problems of immigrant children

a. English-speaking children
Although there will be little communication difficulty with these children there are still many problems. In all probability their previous culture pattern will have been quite different from ours. Even such a simple idea as that of a family becomes complex when different communities are considered.

Mathematical work with these children should take no previous experience for granted, however simple, but be directly related to the immediate present. Whenever possible use should be made of their particular abilities and interests. For example, many West Indian children have a great love for and skill in all forms of movement. Perhaps some at least of their early mathematical work should be based on spatial ideas. But before anything else comes language. Care must be taken to ensure that immigrant children develop their confidence in and use of the English language.

b. Non-English-speaking children
A considerable problem emerges here, particularly in the case of an isolated group of non-English speaking children in an ordinary school community where no special provision can be made. Such mathematics as is introduced to these children should be concerned essentially with communication.

Sometimes communication will be established first through the use of symbols. For example, in one school it was discovered that a group of Pakistani children had formerly attended school in their own country, and could manipulate figures quite effectively. The first communication was, therefore, established through 'sums'.

The introduction of pictorial representation, using data collected from the immediate environment, will be of help in the establishment of communication and will directly foster the growth of language.

Most children are naturally friendly as well as curious, and probably the greatest success will be achieved where children can work in small groups, immigrant and native together.

10 Furniture and equipment

1 Furniture

In the context of a new approach to primary school mathematics a fresh look may be taken at the influence of classroom furniture, much of which in design and arrangement belongs to the era when passive learning predominated.

Desks, as we know them, were designed to meet certain specific needs. The lids sloped to facilitate the growth of the skill of penmanship, they lifted to reveal a space wherein the child stored his exercise books and text-books. They were placed in rows facing the teacher's desk and the blackboard.

Experimental school designs of the last decade have endeavoured realistically to meet the needs of children in the light of current educational thought and practice. Classrooms have disappeared to make way for learning bays, desks have been replaced by practical tables and workbenches; comfortable chairs exist in quiet corners where children can read.

Much, however, can be done even in the most unlikely classrooms, and it is in these that many children and their teachers will have to face the impact of new ways in mathematics. Space is obviously at a premium. There are many classes of forty or more existing in classrooms designed for thirty. It is sometimes helpful for a teacher to estimate the amount of total available floor space and the amount of this valuable space which is taken up by furniture. The startling figures that emerge will spur the teacher on to ask 'How much of this furniture is really essential?' For example, is it really necessary for the teacher's table to be so large? Most classrooms contain some unnecessary clutter, but even when this is cleared away a considerable problem remains. Some teachers have found that it is not essential for a child to have a particular chair and desk for his exclusive use and have disposed of a small number of these thereby releasing valuable floor space. Where stackable furniture exists it can be kept out of the way until needed. It has sometimes been suggested that children need the security of their own chair or place, but surely this has been a matter of conditioning. In nursery and infant schools the children certainly do not lack security for want of a particular place at a desk or table.

Much space can be saved by re-arranging the existing furniture. It is no longer necessary that at all times every child should be able to see the blackboard. They will be working in small groups, and in all probability each group will be engaged in some different activity. Learning bays, or areas of occupation, can be contrived even in a crowded classroom. A cupboard placed at right-angles to, instead of along, a wall is a good beginning. A piece of hardboard or peg-board attached to the back of the cupboard, yet extending upwards, affords valuable additional display space. Screens or even rolls of corrugated cardboard of five-foot depth can also provide not only working privacy but extra display space. Old, tall cupboards, re-positioned to be on their sides, can be converted into admirable lockers which not only provide storage space within and display space on top, but make quite adequate room dividers.

To cover a wide range of practical work it is essential to have flat-topped working surfaces. These can be contrived by placing desks together and propping up the lids with corks, pieces of sponge or something similar. An old blackboard covered with Fablon, or a piece of hardboard, will provide a continuous working surface when this is necessary. Frequently, when given the choice, children prefer to work standing at these improvised tables. If this is so then stacking the chairs out of the way will give even greater freedom of movement.

In some schools additional space can be found in corridor, cloakroom, or entrance hall. At the very least these places will supply valuable additional display space used perhaps for topics which involve and interest the whole school.

A conventional junior classroom

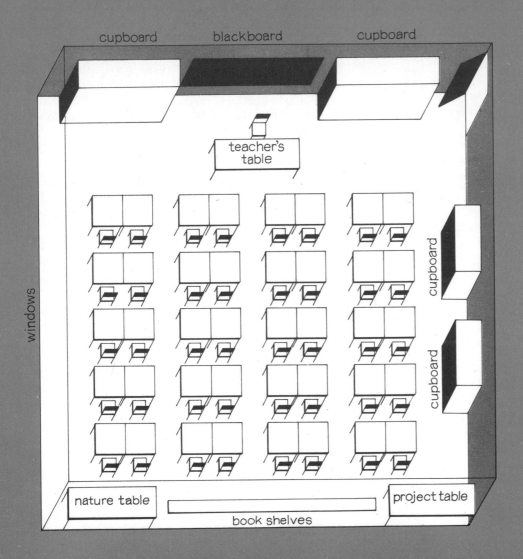

cupboard blackboard cupboard

teacher's table

windows

cupboard

cupboard

nature table

book shelves

project table

A Teacher's table

B Lockers containing equipment for mathematics, possibly made from old, tall cupboard

C Books on mathematics

D Cupboard containing equipment for mathematics and science, possibly those items that need to be locked away at night

E Cupboard containing materials for art and craft work

F Table for display

G Painting easels

The same classroom re-arranged to make better provision for active learning

H Woodwork bench

I Area reserved for reading

J Uncommitted area for the sudden unpredictable interest that requires space

K Lockers, similar to B, containing general scientific materials

L Table for display

M Scientific books

N Corrugated cardboard, depth 5 feet

X Chairs stacked out of the way.

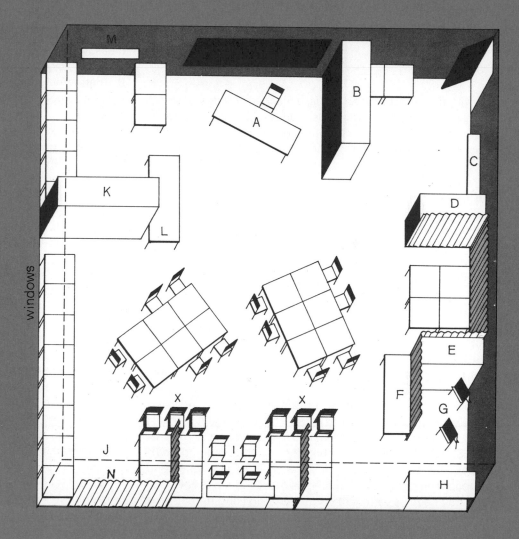

In one school the children were all involved in some work concerning the wind. Among other activities hydrogen-filled balloons were released daily. Many of these balloons were recovered and returned to the school. Records of the number of balloons returned and the distances and directions were displayed in the entrance hall where all children, teachers and even parents could see them and keep abreast of current information.

2 Materials

The type of work suggested in these teachers' guides is bound to involve a variety of materials, some relatively expensive, most of them relatively cheap; some bulky, others quite small. Perhaps the most helpful division is into raw materials and measuring devices.

Raw materials
These will include such things as
a. clay, plasticine, bricks, sand and water
b. dried peas, beans, rice, conkers and nails
c. matchboxes, cotton reels, spills, milk straws, pipe cleaners, Dinky toys and poppet beads.

Storage is the important issue here. All materials should be adequately stored in suitable containers, clearly labelled, in a precise position in the classroom. For example, peas and rice should be kept in transparent screw-top containers, possibly glass but preferably plastic. Clay, sand and water not only need suitable containers, but children need to be provided with suitable conditions in which these things may be satisfactorily handled. Large sheets of polythene, adequate aprons, cloths, brushes and pans are just as important as the material itself. Children need to learn that, for example, different tools and techniques are used in filling a tin with (a) water, and (b) peas. The provision of materials makes this possible. The water tray needs a variety of containers, jugs and funnels; the jar of peas needs a variety of scoops and spoons. As none of these materials involve excessive expenditure it should be possible for each class to have its own suitable range of materials.

Measuring devices
Children will require many measuring devices, increasing in complexity as they get older. These will include:

a. balances, spring balances, scales and weights, both British and Continental.
b. rulers, yardsticks, tape measures, surveyors' tapes and chains, map measurers, compasses, micrometers and metric measures
c. timers, clocks and stop watches
d. thermometers
e. plastic containers, watering cans, British and Continental measures.

Expense is involved here, but the criterion must always be that of quality. Inadequate tools only lead to frustration, and one really good pair of scales is far better value than five inaccurate ones. This kind of equipment should be assembled gradually and in accordance with the direction of interests both of children and teachers. As the range of interests and enquiry extends so will the range of materials.

The next question is how and where measuring devices should be stored. In the first instance it is more than likely that some of these things will have to be shared between classes. The same principles of storage will apply. The equipment should be kept in suitable containers, clearly labelled, and in a precise position: in this case perhaps a common cupboard in hall or corridor, or if housed in a classroom then in a place of easy access for children from other classes. Some teachers have found that the expensive smaller items need a different kind of provision, and so have kept things like micrometers and stop watches in their own drawers. This may, indeed, be necessary in the early stages of the work.

There are, of course, many other materials that will be used in this work which have not been covered in either of the above categories. Such things as string, adhesives, scissors, felt pens, paper and cardboard, are used in many activities.

A group of three, one using a measuring device, the other two counting and then recording their findings

Specific equipment normally associated with a different subject, for example, a globe, will also be used on occasions. The most important issue here is the availability of the materials and equipment. To store things at the top of high cupboards, or in the inner sanctum of the stock room, is just not appropriate. If the materials are readily available then the work will proceed smoothly.

3 The mathematics room

In some schools, materials and equipment have been housed centrally in a special room devoted solely to mathematical work. There are advantages and disadvantages here.

It can be very advantageous to have certain specific materials and equipment housed in a particular room where they need never be disturbed. In some schools such a room serves as a workshop for children during school hours and teachers in the evenings. Children move freely in and out of the workshop during the day, selecting the equipment they need, carrying out their experiments, and recording their findings.

Schools which are short of money, but not space, will find that by housing materials centrally in a mathematics room more children can benefit from the limited supply of materials.

Setting up a mathematics room could, however, act against the whole spirit of the work if it were used in the manner of the secondary school laboratory. In this case the children would perhaps have a timetabled period per day in this room, possibly taught by a mathematics specialist. Not only is the time limitation apparent (they would have to stop their activities at a certain moment if another class was waiting outside) but there is a likelihood that mathematics would not become part of the general pattern of learning intermingling with other subjects.

4 Responsibilities

The provision of materials and equipment is of little value unless the mutual responsibility of both teacher and child is clearly defined within the general pattern of class relationships.

The responsibility of the teacher is to
a. assemble the necessary materials — gradually to allow for the growth and development of ideas;
b. organise adequate storage — clearly labelled jars and boxes;
c. introduce new tools and equipment with great care, ensuring that the children understand the purpose, possibilities and perhaps the delicacy of the new instrument; and
d. *trust* the children to use the material.

The child, too, has an important part to play. He has to take the responsibility for
a. selecting the most suitable materials to enable him to solve his problem;
b. using the materials with care — doing any necessary clearing up;
c. returning the materials after use to their particular storage place.

It is worth remembering in these days of crises and shortages that the skill and time of the teacher should be used to best advantage. It could well be argued that time spent in unlocking cupboards, selecting and giving out material is time needed for more valuable work. If the classroom structure is designed to enable the children to take real responsibility for these things then the teacher will have more time to spend for being with the children discussing their problems and guiding them on to further progress.

11 Communication

1 Mathematics books

Conventional text books and exercise books

It has been customary for children in primary schools to work through blocks of text-book examples in their study of arithmetic. The books concerned were variable in quality, but were usually very carefully graded. It became inevitable that the subject matter of the school arithmetic syllabus should be virtually identical with the contents of the *text* book.

Children working from text books normally used exercise books. The computational exercises which appeared in the text book were copied into the exercise book and the child then worked the *exercise*. It was in this context that the considerations mentioned in Chapter 1 — meticulous presentation and accurate computation — were demonstrated.

Other books

In recent years there has been an enormous increase in both the quantity and quality of books produced for children, and there is now available a wide variety of books concerning mathematics. Some of these might be referred to as *topic books*, others would be termed *library* or *reference books*; many of them are delightfully produced. There are also some new-style text books on mathematics.

The use of books

Teachers are faced with the problem of deciding not only which books to select for their classroom, but how best to use them. Predominantly these books should be source books for ideas — in the first instance, perhaps ideas for the teacher. Later they will be used by children as points of reference and sources of information. They will also provide starting points for investigation. This dual purpose is very important. Children will gradually learn that books can not only help them to solve but also to pose problems; some children,

browsing among a collection of such books have come across seemingly conflicting information, and have been stimulated to make enquiries of their own in the same field.

Ideally a collection of such books should exist in every classroom, easily accessible and attractively displayed. In the early stages of this work, however, there will probably be insufficient money available for distribution on this scale and some form of central collection of mathematics books will be necessary. These should be housed in an easily accessible place, such as corridor, hall or possibly the school library. As the collection grows it will be possible to build up a supply of books for each classroom, even if this involves more than one copy of some of the books.

It is generally agreed that children learning mathematics through their own discoveries nevertheless need a little systematic practice at computation. Some of those teaching on such lines have made use of their traditional text books to meet this need. For example, if a group of children had come across a problem involving division of money the teacher would discuss it with them in the context of the real situation, help them to acquire this new skill, and might then find a few suitable examples from a text book, or perhaps better, might select examples from a number of text books, to give them a little extra practice in the skill.

Compared with the step by step approach, working chapter by chapter through a well-tried text book, this suggested use of books may appear to be rather haphazard. As with all other aspects of the work the transition must be gradual. Slowly a pattern will emerge from the child's exploration of his environment. It will be different in kind from the pattern imposed by the use of graded text books, but of far greater interest and value to children and teachers.

2 The assignment card

A card with a mathematical question on it, however simple or complex, is sometimes called a *job card*, a *work card* or an *assignment card*. In a sense these cards are a development from a *sum card* which was an early attempt to give a more individual flavour than was possible when all the children worked from the same *sum book;* for, on analysis, it appeared that sum cards frequently did no more than reproduce a page from a sum book. This situation must be guarded against when assignment cards are being considered. These cards must do more than suggest a problem involving some form of measurement or mental agility with numbers. These things are important, but the assignment card must also foster active thought, leading to the forming of judgements and the taking of decisions.

A card for a young child might read:
>**How many acorns balance the big pebble?**

It would be considerably enhanced by the additional instruction – *Guess first.*
Later on an important addition might be:
>**Comment on your results.**

In order to develop awareness and sensitivity, cards might contain the phrase:
>**What do you notice?**
>or
>**What do you discover?**

After some experience in this kind of work the suggested problem might be followed by such a question as:
>**Can you see a pattern?**
>, or
>**Is there a relationship?**

It is when the child reaches this stage of his assignment that discussion with the teacher is most profitable. It is the teacher's skilful questions during this discussion which will lead the child to make the discovery – perceive the patterns and relationships within his recorded data – if he has not yet the ability or maturity to do this on his own.

We have been accustomed to think of evaluating children's work in mathematics in terms of an answer which is either right or wrong. Some assignment cards will undoubtedly fit into this category demanding a definitive, numerical answer. Others will lead up to the discovery of a relationship, for example the relationship between the length of side and the area of a square. Still others will have no clear end in view other than developing in the child an awareness in a new field of mathematics, for example a card suggesting that the child should investigate certain shapes in the environment and asking for comments on his findings. Assignment cards for any group of children should include examples from all three categories. Indeed some cards may require responses of each of these types, prompted by an investigation of the same situation.

Doubts are sometimes raised as to the suitability of the assignment card when there are children present who cannot as yet read. Two important issues emerge here. It will be agreed that no child should be prevented from enjoying this kind of work through his inability, as yet, to master the skill of reading. Where a spirit of co-operation exists in a class those who can read will gladly come to the rescue of those who cannot. On the other hand, many teachers have found that children have made great progress in reading through the use of assignment cards. They realise that the work is exciting; motivation is therefore strong. At the simplest level the child will match the word *conkers* on his assignment card with a label *conkers* on the appropriate box. From such simple beginnings can the skill of reading grow.

There are, of course, dangers inherent in the use of assignment cards. It would be possible for a teacher to prepare a selection of assignment cards at the beginning of the year, and for the rest of the year the children would systematically work through them. This would represent a tremendous advance in that the children would be actively involved with real materials. The danger would lie in the possibility that, in time, the situation might become over-familiar and this approach might become as stereotyped as the old use of a text book. There are probably three stages through which this kind of work might progress.

Stage 1

The introduction of the first assignment cards based on the ideas of the teacher. These ideas will have been culled from teachers' courses, from source books of mathematical ideas, or perhaps from the Nuffield teachers' guides.

Stage 2

The further development of the assignment cards in order to relate the work to the specific school environment and the particular interests of the children.

Stage 3

The partial or even total discarding of assignment cards as more and more of the work arises spontaneously within the framework of normal school activities. (Cf. for example, the investigations concerning goal circles, the observation of birds and the discussion on man-hole covers described earlier.)

Much of the work in infant schools is already in the Stage 3 category as a result of developments during the post-war years. But the sequence of stages may become appropriate again with the introduction of new topics, or with the more mature apprciation of familiar ones.

Looked at in this way the assignment card is seen as a firm and quite lengthy bridge between the exclusive use of a text book and the ultimate realisation that the 'environment' in its wide sense (see Chapter 6) can provide all the necessary stimuli for the young mathematical 'researcher'.

3   Recording

When children are learning mathematics through their own discoveries the question arises as to *when* and *in what manner* their work should be recorded. The sole use of a standard exercise book has, in many cases, been found to be inadequate and unsuitable.

In some schools children use large books containing unlined paper for their personal mathematics work. Other schools use folders into which children put separate pieces of paper containing the records of their work. Class folios are sometimes used to contain large items of group work, which after being hung up on display for a while take their place in the folio.

The question of how and when to record has been under discussion for many years in infant schools. There comes a time when the skill of writing emerges and is used with joy by young children. At this stage they will write endless stories that ramble on and on with little regard for sequence, punctuation or any of the adult skills. Nevertheless this is an important time as far as recording mathematical experiences is concerned, for at this stage when the children are anxious to write, one of the main tasks of the teacher is to ensure that the children have a wide variety of experiences to write about. The first recording of personal mathematical experiences will, therefore, be seen to be in the use of words, employing an ever-increasing range of mathematical vocabulary gained through discussion with the teacher.

At much the same time group experiences are likely to be recorded in some form of pictorial representation in two or three dimensions. The first kind of recording – in words – is of a personal nature and it would be appropriate if it occurred in the child's individual work book. The second kind of recording is suitable for display in order to provoke discussion among other children in the class.

There are important considerations to be weighed up at this stage. It is at this level that children can be introduced to a wide variety of recording techniques, the use of many different three-dimensional materials for early pictorial work, different approaches to two-dimensional recording, and the use of many different qualities, colours, types, ruling and sizes of paper. Moreover, some consideration should be given to arguments for and against recording. Many teachers have found that, although every experience demands discussion, it is perhaps not essential that every experience should be recorded. The criterion should be whether the recording enhances or detracts from the quality of the experience. For many children recording too much and too soon has made a drudgery of their mathematical work. This can be disastrous in the early formation of wrong attitudes towards mathematics. If it seems desirable that the experience should be recorded then an appropriately high standard of recording should be expected. Children will gladly rise to such an occasion and produce delightful block graphs and their very best handwriting. The sense of occasion is important if this standard of work is to be achieved. Teachers must have the courage of their convictions over this matter, and accept that, in many instances, at the end of an exciting experience there may be nothing to show on paper — although much may be recaptured in subsequent discussion and conversation.

If this kind of approach is adopted in the first years of the primary school not only will standards of recording have been set, but older children will be enabled to make effective choices as to the kind of recording that is appropriate for any given experience. In many cases they will choose to record an experience in several different ways, realising that if no clear pattern arises in one format it may appear through the use of a different technique.

12 Evaluating progress

1 Records kept by a child
2 Records kept by a class teacher
3 Records kept by the head teacher
4 Traditional attainment tests
5 Record keeping and staffing problems

There are many problems that arise through the introduction and development of new approaches to the learning of mathematics, yet none is more difficult than the problem of evaluating progress. 'How can I keep track of what the children are doing?' and 'How do I know how far they have got?' are two of the questions commonly asked by teachers. There are no easy answers to these questions. In time each school and each teacher will find solutions to meet their particular needs.

1 Records kept by a child

Children much enjoy keeping records of their own. In some schools they keep individual school diaries in which they record their daily activities. Such diaries would include entries concerning activities in the field of mathematics. These would naturally be highly subjective but, nevertheless, of considerable value, for in turning back the pages the child can refresh his memory as to the range of activities he has attempted during the last month, term or even year. It is not unusual for a dormant interest to be reawakened and approached again in a new way through the use of this kind of school diary.

Where assignment cards are used records of progress can be kept through the use of a chart fixed on the classroom wall. (See diagram on next page)

When a child or children have carried out an assignment, have discussed it fully with the teacher, have decided whether, and in what way, to record, and have completed the recording, then this card is duly ticked off and dated on the chart.

In some classrooms wall space is at a premium and teachers prefer not to use this valuable space in such a way. An alternative method is to use an ordinary exercise book. (See diagram on next page)

The book is usually kept in some suitable place at the centre of the mathematical activity. In this way, too, children and teachers have an opportunity of assessing the range and number of experiences the children have had in any given period of time. Allowing children to undertake some responsibility for the keeping of records seems not only to enhance interest but also to make possible an individual sense of achievement and progress.

2 Records kept by a class teacher

It is customary for teachers to keep some kind of general record book in which the week's activities, interests, achievements and failures, are recorded. In some schools, separate subjects are given individual treatment in these record books.

The mathematics section of such a record book would contain information as to the topics being investigated during the week. Other schools, working perhaps within a more flexible framework, keep weekly class diaries of a more general nature. These diaries contain a record of everything interesting that evolved during the week, taking particular note of the unexpected. For example, a group of children aged between 6 and 9 in an urban school were taken on a visit to a country market. The visit was designed to give the children some experience of the range of local-grown fruit and vegetables, and to enable them to see and learn about a variety of farm-yard animals. The teachers' diaries for the week expressed astonishment at the amount of unexpected mathematical work that derived from this experience.

Within these general diaries many teachers make entries concerning individual children. At first sight the records may seem haphazard for there is no attempt to make entries about each child every week. The teachers try to record *significant* occasions, advances or difficulties. A sudden, unexpected demonstration of mathematical insight would merit an entry

Suggested wall chart Diagram 1

Assignment cards are numbered but need not be worked in order.
Child completes this record,
e.g. S. M. Brown completed Assignment Card 6 on March 28th.

NAMES	1	2	3	4	5	6	7	8	9	10	11	12	13	14	15	16	17	18
J Adams			✓26/3															
P Arundel																		
B Baker				✓1/3														
SM Brown						✓28/3												

as would an unexpected difficulty. Unusually sustained interest and effort would also be worthy of record. A sequence of such records can easily disclose a story of a child's mathematical efforts, triumphs and reverses that would otherwise be unsuspected.

Teachers using this kind of weekly diary find that, in addition, they need to keep a separate record of the progress of individual children. Sometimes this is in the form of a card index using a separate card for each child. Another common method is the use of a loose-leaf file or folder with each child being allocated a separate sheet. These cards or sheets would be compiled from all other forms of record kept by the child or the teacher, and might contain

a. a list of assignments satisfactorily completed on topics covered – with dates;

b. highlights of the child's progress including setbacks as well as achievements;

c. a note on particular difficulties;

d. some periodic evaluation by the teacher as to the child's attitude towards as well as achievements in mathematics.

Some teachers find it helpful to keep specific examples of children's work, which, if carefully filed, form a record in themselves. They must, of course, be ordinary routine examples, and not special pieces of work undertaken for the purpose. For example, one teacher keeps the first and last booklet of the term; another files the first effort completed each month.

3   Records kept by the head teacher

Head teachers will, in the main, require to keep two different kinds of records. One of these will be concerned with the general development of mathematics within the school, the other with individual progress and attainment.

The first of these will probably represent a synopsis of the diaries kept by the class teachers. Having compiled a statement outlining the scope and nature of the mathematics work to be attempted in the school the head teacher will require evidence as to the substance with which the outline is being filled in, and the manner of doing this. It is in the light of this evidence that such an initial appraisal can be satisfactorily amended year by year. This record will contain a review of topics being covered, take note of contemporary interests, and slowly reveal an emerging pattern within the mathematical activities of the school. It will enable the head teacher to perceive certain seeming anomalies and initiate speedy investigation. For example, it might appear that both 6- and 10-year-olds have been measuring the playground. The head teacher will need to know more precisely just how the two different age groups are approaching the work and what they are getting from it. The same environmental starting point can provide mathematical stimulus for almost any age range within the primary school, yet the quality of the experience should differ greatly according to the ability and the maturity of the children.

Through the use of this kind of diary the head teacher will be able to notice the gaps that appear in the children's experience. Some gaps are almost inevitable when the work is approached in this way. When significant gaps become apparent recommendations can be made that at a certain stage a particular teacher should endeavour to contrive experience for the children in order to fill such gaps.

The second kind of record the head teacher will need is some kind of assessment of individual children, if possible objective as well as subjective, to be completed at regular intervals, possibly six monthly or annually. The fact must be faced that this is a time-consuming job, for to be of value any tests must be individual, and must endeavour to assess the child's progress in the field of concept-formation. For years now busy head teachers have been finding the time to assess each child individually in the matter of his progress in reading, and have kept records of this, perhaps in terms of the child's reading age. What is now necessary is that mathematical progress should be assessed in a similar manner, through individual contact between the child and the assessor (probably the head teacher). Tests deriving from those devised by Professor Piaget and used as a basis for his research in Geneva and elsewhere are now being used for this purpose.

Assignments completed or
Topics investigated

Spring Term
1965

Name

Date of birth

Highlights of Progress

Particular difficulties

Teacher's evaluation

Interest in them is being fostered in teachers' study groups. What will eventually be needed is some kind of standardisation from among the wide range of available tests in the field of concept-formation, and work is in progress on this.

4   Traditional attainment tests

Conventional attainment tests have aimed primarily at the measurement of the child's ability to manipulate numbers speedily and accurately; they have represented the principal manner in which children's progress was measured, as arithmetic tests of this nature were presented at regular intervals. In the light of recent developments it will be seen that the evidence produced from the results of such tests cannot present a complete picture of the child's mathematical development. Carefully planned attainment tests can, nevertheless, provide useful evidence of progress, to be added to all other accumulated records concerning interest, attitude and achievement, all of which should be set against the more objective data obtained from the individual tests involving concept-formation.

5   Record keeping and staffing problems

The keeping of records as suggested here is bound to take time, yet today these records are not only desirable, they are essential. New teachers, temporary teachers, supply teachers, part-time teachers all need the maximum possible evidence to help them in their planning. There should be evidence of individual, group and class activity, of interests, achievements and difficulties.

The teacher thrust into an unfamiliar classroom need not feel bewildered if the system is running smoothly, as the children will be only too delighted to explain what they're doing. But it is better still if the children themselves can produce their own records of progress. In any case it is essential to have the previous teacher's records for reference. There can be no hope of continuity or consistency in children's mathematical activity if adequate records do not exist. It must be the responsibility of each and every teacher to ensure that they do.

13 Conclusion

A great many problems have been posed in this book, and only a few possible solutions have been tentatively suggested. This is almost inevitable, for at this stage no-one would claim to be in a position from which he could make definitive statements concerning the place, purpose or content of a primary school programme in mathematics. The experience of recent years has, nevertheless, enabled the problem to be more clearly formulated, and more minds are now being brought to bear on it. There is widespread interest among mathematicians, psychologists, primary school teachers and parents.

Of one thing, however, we can be sure. We are educating young children for an unknown and quite unpredictable future. The pattern of our industrial society is changing rapidly. Many of today's 5-year-olds, when they leave school, will gain employment in spheres as yet unthought of. A significant proportion of the working population will find, at some time in the future, that their jobs are obsolete. They will have to undergo re-training for a job that as yet no-one has envisaged. The working week will get shorter, and people will have an increasing amount of leisure time.

It is against this background that any suggested programme of primary school mathematics should be set. Children must be given experiences designed to encourage flexibility and adaptability, and to foster creative thinking. They will need to develop resources to cope confidently with a constantly changing environment. Such resources for ordering, perhaps controlling, even predicting events or experiences will principally be developed through the exploration of a classroom environment that, in some measure, reflects the changing world beyond.

Children are endowed with natural curiosity, which will lead them to investigate an environment that is rich, varied, ever-changing and quite irresistible. Such explorations will develop a sense of adventure, and lead to the delight of achievement. More than this, the children may even experience a sense of wonder and excitement as they gain insight into the relationships that constitute the world of mathematics.

Appendix 1

How I started
by J. W. G. Boucher

I had fifty very bright top-year juniors in an above average junior school, and with the common entrance examination completed, the usual thoughts regarding activities to keep interests alive loomed large.

Creative English and project work in social studies were already planned but mathematics (arithmetic) still disturbed me. Side-tracking into elementary geometry and algebra did not seem to be the answer and further mental, mechanical and problems would be a complete waste of time.

After consultations with my headmaster and the district H.M.I. it was decided that I should try a more practical approach through

> mathematics in geography
> simple surveying
> inaccessible heights using clinometers, etc.
> polyhedra
> simple navigation.

This called for group work and a flexible timetable. Before groups of children were dispersed to their allotted tasks, class discussions took place to familiarise them with maps, grids, the compass, angular measurement and the protractor, scale, symbols (Ordinance Survey maps), etc. Simple clinometers were made in the craft lesson.

Groups of eight children were then given an assignment of work. Two groups were sent to work around the school or in the school playing field. When these returned to the classroom to write up their discoveries another two groups were sent out. As each day passed, more and more of the class became involved in group mathematics. We began to use the school canteen as much as possible because of the more suitable, large, flat-topped tables. A pattern had developed with some children working outside, some in the canteen and some in the classroom. My time was spent moving among the various groups to offer constructive criticism or pose additional questions, but I soon found that more often I would be in the classroom discussing work which a group had completed or 'marking' a finished assignment which had been recorded for inclusion in their mathematics folders. This meant that I had to trust children to work without supervision and I was not disappointed.

Generally the children worked until a task was completed, which meant incursions into the set timetable. As this was fairly flexible anyway, no harm was done and time for other subjects was made up as and when felt necessary.

After six months with this class and an experimental mathematics programme I moved to a very different school with children of varied I.Q.s and home backgrounds.

Ministry courses and topical reading matter gave me further incentives to continue the new approach, and with children of third-year, mixed abilities.

It seemed that the background to the new approach was as follows:

Make it as practical as possible
Create a mathematical climate
Promote understanding and interest
Reduce the mechanical drudgery of 'doing sums'
Encourage discovery and other ways of solving a problem
Treat mathematics as a whole and not as 'mental, mechanical and problems'
Foster discussion. Let them talk and learn from each other
Find mathematics in other subjects
Use real situation and the environment
Keep it interesting and make mathematics more pleasant.

After perusing the reigning mathematics syllabus and bearing in mind the other aspects of mathematics that I now wished to include, I started to make assignment cards which I thought were suitable for my children.

I tried several methods of 'grouping' the children but finally found that groups of three, of compatible ability, were the best arrangement. Mixed ability groupings seemed a failure because of the intolerance of the bright child for the less able children.

One group at a time (one per day) was introduced to the new way of working in the mathematics period. Three or four groups were then allowed to work at their various assignments whilst the rest of the class did other work, sometimes traditional arithmetic but, often, something which they enjoyed doing, e.g. curve stitching, mathematical models.

More and more assignment cards were needed and, eventually, it seemed necessary to have about forty of these. They were made from coloured card and covered with polythene. The colour of the card denoted a particular aspect of mathematics:

green for simple surveying
pink for money
blue for time
white for shape and size, and so on.

A record chart was kept on the classroom wall and children ticked off an assignment against their names when it was completed to my satisfaction.   (See next page)

The assignment cards were not necessarily progressive but about six dealing with each aspect, perhaps measurement of weight or speed, gave a variety of experiences dealing with the same concept. It was perhaps true that the first two cards were a simple introduction to the problem and the less able children always did these first.

Apparatus was largely 'home-made' in the initial stages or acquired by the children from home: abaci, clinometers, nail-boards, boxes for sand-filling, etc., lino tiles, old clocks, train sets, Dinky toys, timetables, maps and globes. Purchases were then made on requisition of: stop-watches, map measurers, surveyor's tapes, surveyor's chain, click-wheels, Ordinance Survey maps, mariner's compass, direc-

tion finders, ranging rods, scales and balances, felt pens, large graph paper and books of reference.

Parents' open evenings were organised to display the type of mathematics that the children were doing and this was followed by P.T.A. fund-raising activities to purchase more equipment.

The children carried out the recording in jotters. Their notes and discoveries were then discussed and, if thought worthwhile, expounded and recorded again for their mathematics folder or, perhaps, for wall display. From the children's discoveries came opportunities for tabulation in various forms, graphical representation and, most important, a fair amount of written English.

The class timetable, as a consequence of the children's interest and keenness to finish a job, was necessarily as flexible as matters would allow. The whole class was not necessarily engaged in mathematics at the same time. If a group of children had been absorbed in mathematics for two whole mornings then they probably did no mathematics the next day but were directed towards some other subject.

Classroom furnishings had to be considered and unwanted furniture was removed to make as much space as possible for flat-topped tables. Display boards were fitted around the walls and tables placed in the corridors until, eventually, a spare room became available as a mathematics room. It may be of interest to mention here that, in spite of the acquisition of a mathematics room, other teachers in the school seldom used this, preferring to use their own classroom and other facilities available.

Throughout the school it became a common practice for children to make their own observations of the mathematics around them. This seemed to be a good starting point. Weather recordings, attendance, meal and milk records, growth of plants, the lengthening and shortening of shadows, days, etc., were all observed and recorded, usually by some form of pictorial representation.

	NAVY						RED						GREEN						WHITE						YELLOW						BLUE		
	1	2	3	4	5	6	1	2	3	4	5	6	1	2	3	4	5	6	1	2	3	4	5	6	1	2	3	4	5	6	1	2	3
B WILSON			✓				✓	✓								✓				✓							✓						
P BLAKE	✓	✓						✓					✓	✓						✓					✓								
C CHADWICK			✓				✓	✓						✓									✓			✓							
W HAWORTH			✓				✓	✓						✓													✓						
J TOPPING	✓													✓																			
L FREATHY	✓													✓																			

Personal data, i.e.
sizes of shoes
waist
heights
weights.

Class data, i.e.
birthdays
brothers and sisters
cars owned by parents
pocket money, etc.
television programmes.

All these projects were carried out to stimulate interest and use the real situation from which mathematics could be extracted.

Children often asked for, and were given, something to do for 'homework' during week-ends or holidays:

'The geometry I see around me'
'Plan of our house'
'Mathematics from a car ride'

Often, a piece of work would be displayed and whole-class discussion took place concerning the particular topic. This was most valuable and helped spoken English a good deal. It also encouraged thinking and reasoning, especially when questions were posed such as

'How can we find out?' or
'Is there a better way of doing this?'

An example of the type of situation which seems to spring from nowhere yet leads to some valuable, spontaneous work is contained in the following:

A 9-year-old boy had made a five-barred gate from card-board. The whole class was shown this and some discussion followed. They were then asked to write about the gate during an English lesson. Needless to say, every child also drew the gate!

From their discussion and written work the following vocabulary resulted: horizontal, vertical, diagonal, parallel, hinged, rigid, strengthen, angles, etc.

Mathematically, the children had observed and denoted on their drawing those angles which were the same, those which were different and the right-angles. No mention was made at this stage of corresponding, alternative, or vertically opposite angles, but a valuable foundation had been laid towards the more formal understanding of these.

A check was kept on the children's abilities in computation. Duplicated sheets of mental, mechanical or written problems were used whenever it seemed appropriate: in the early days, because of examinations of this kind, a crash programme of a week's work was undertaken as preparation. If certain children were found to have a weakness in any particular computation then practice, after practical situations, was given in this way. Copying down of sums from blackboard or text book disappeared completely. From such checks it appeared that there was, perhaps, a 5 per cent drop in speed and accuracy tests, hardly anything to worry about, and perhaps a fairer reflection of a child's true ability. No doubt the same drop in attainment would be noticeable after a school holiday! However, on the credit side it is far more important to reveal that attainment in written problems was at least 5 per cent better.

Discipline presented no new problems. The same mischief occurred as will always occur with young children. Initially rubber bands, etc., presented tempting opportunities. However, when children are interested and curious to discover something for themselves, they have little time for anything else. Noise too diminishes as interest is awakened and they settle down to their tasks. Mild rebukes were sometimes necessary but as the children got used to the new approach I am certain that they found there was no novelty in useless chatter or wasting time.

A few helpful suggestions towards organisation of the new method of teaching would include:

i. Make certain the children know what to do.

ii. Appoint group leaders to obtain apparatus and, more important, put it back.

iii. Keep apparatus in a set place, e.g. weight corner, map drawer, measuring corner (scales, etc.).

iv. Keep stop-watches, map measurers and pocket compasses, in the teacher's drawer. These are attractive to children.

v. Don't expect children to record everything they do in mathematics.

vi. Pose additional verbal questions concerning an assignment and get the children to make up additional questions of their own. This can also help when you are harassed by more than one group of children.

Finally, I am certain that the results of a practical approach to mathematics are not all seen at the time of doing it in the junior school. Its real value, we hope, is realised later in the secondary school.

Appendix 2

How I began
by G. B. Corston

This article was originally planned as the thoughts of one headmaster on how the teaching of mathematics developed in his school, but after turning this over in my mind for several days in such different places as train journeys to Blackpool and Folkestone, and visiting schools to talk to children and teachers and to see what they were doing in mathematics, it is difficult to say when and how it really began. Although it may not have any direct practical bearing on how to start new approaches to mathematics in school from a headmaster's point of view, and although it may not help to solve any of the attendant problems, I must say that contrary to the experiences of many teachers the seeds were sown in my own school days from about the age of 11. I know now that I was fortunate to be influenced by one inspired and enlightened teacher at grammar school. In the present situation this emphasises the influence of the teacher in the classroom, for this man taught with two ideas — that mathematics should be enjoyable, and that one of the primary considerations is to teach from conviction. He was convinced that it should be enjoyable and hence, that there need be no fear of mathematics — and we were convinced too. Later these seeds began to grow and flourish at training college where I was again fortunate to be influenced on what I now know to be the right lines in mathematics by, among others, Mrs. E. M. Williams. But, although there may not appear to be any direct bearing on mathematics in the primary school, equally as important was the fact that while I studied mathematics and science at college, the college authorities had the good sense to see that I also took such subjects as English literature and creative activities — art, craft, and so on — and we were always encouraged to write in a creative way. One might well say, 'What has all this to do with the problems of a head teacher wishing to start new ideas of teaching mathematics in his school?'. Of course, it will not help him with the practical side of what to do, but I feel that somehow, unconsciously perhaps, these early days have influenced my thinking.

But to come nearer to the present day, in 1954 I was appointed head of a five-form junior mixed school in a very old building. At that time in that school the classes were mixed-ability, of necessity, groups, and although mathematics was largely arithmetic from text books, at least the teachers were forced to teach classes of forty-five as individuals, or in several groups. Some practical work was done but I can see, in retrospect, that it was only scratching the surface and mathematically, I suppose, was of little value as it was largely 'practical arithmetic' for its own sake and little more. Two years later, in 1956, I moved as head of a new two-form entry junior school. But for some time the mathematics was still taught from books, and although I laid emphasis on 'understanding' in schemes of work I suggested, I am sure this meant 'understanding' of techniques — how to do subtraction by equal additions, for instance, rather than principles involved. My main concern at that time was with language, and mathematics, I suppose, was left out in the cold. I was blessed with a staff of gifted and enterprising teachers who thought on much the same lines as I did and our main consideration was to get away from English lessons as 'English Exercises' and 'Composition' and to see that language permeated all the work of the school. Within three years we had built up a library of some 1,500 books (now over 2,000), both fiction and information, with similar libraries in the various classrooms, and these were widely used.

Opportunities were constantly created for discussion in all subjects; written work instead of 'exercises' developed in the shape of class newspapers, magazines, nature and science records, and independent historical and geographical studies. It will be noticed that there is no mention of mathematics, but very soon we realised that our other work was showing us that 'sums' were not enough. Science had been introduced in the fourth-year classes with an 'experimental' approach — children 'doing and finding out' — and some mathematics was coming from this. The teacher of one of the fourth-year classes had hit upon the idea of the 'editors' of magazines produced in his class 'paying contributors by cheque', and a study of money, banking, and many calculations arose incidentally from this. When the 11+ tests were over in February I took these fourth-year children once or twice a week for 'lessons' which involved us in doing mathematics outside the school, such as simple surveying; other mathematics arose in planning visits and school journeys. And I found that these activities could best be carried out with the children working in small groups. At about that time all the primary and secondary head teachers in the borough met to discuss working out common 'methods' of doing sums, so that children could transfer from one school to another and pick up the threads quickly. This was certainly a good idea, but after getting involved in a friendly argument about the ways of doing subtraction, I thought that what we had discussed did not go far enough. So gradually, through many small influences, we were being made to look at the mathematics teaching in the school. Then in 1959, two men teachers who were taking classes of 7- and 8-year-olds asked if they could forget about 'sums' from books and approach the number work with these young children by using such things as abaci, number ladders, number strips and squares. It was a small beginning and we didn't progress much further than this, but it did mean that we were delaying the introduction of computation as 'sums' in the early stages, and doing some practical mathematics which had a purpose with the older children. And there it remained for a year or two. Put in other words, I suppose it could be said that in the lower classes the work in number progressed from the practical to the abstract, and that in the upper classes some of the mechanical computation arose from real problems.

At this stage the school roll was some twenty or so above that for which the school was designed, which resulted in large classes and little space in rooms for storage of apparatus and equipment which we were gradually acquiring for science and mathematics, particularly for older children. As I wanted what little apparatus we had to be available for anyone to use, it was stored in a cupboard and on tables in the corridor, readily accessible to any class. This may be one way of overcoming storage problems in crowded schools. It had one drawback. If a piece of equipment on one of the tables had not been used for about two days it soon became covered in a layer of dust — for the cleaners were afraid to touch such precious material.

Promotion caused staff changes, but I still had a nucleus of the original staff who believed in my ideas. Early in 1961, for various reasons, the extension of 'discovery' science to other classes; the appreciation that although we were doing something mathematics was still very much a subject on its own; and also a strong feeling that my work as a head was not extending me enough intellectually (after five years in this school I was becoming mentally stagnant), I turned my attention to the mathematics teaching in the school in a more determined way than previously. It is at this point that I feel my experiences in my own school days were probably beginning to have an effect. Anyhow, I attended courses, I read, I thought. The outcome was that by the end of the 1961–62 year I decided to widen the scope of the mathematics with the youngest children and to introduce a few ideas other than number and computation in the other classes, but not to the same extent. This meant buying more apparatus and materials for activities involving weighing and measuring of all kinds, Dienes' MAB structural material, card and plastic material for work on shapes, and so on. With the older children much of the apparatus we had acquired for science could be used for mathematics. But how to start? In all fairness I felt it was too much to ask the staff to do it as, although they were behind me completely in accepting that something needed to be done, they were at a loss about what to do. So I spent much of the summer holiday preparing some three dozen 'assignments' for the young children in the first year to use. These were simple tasks involving weighing, measuring, money (we used real money), time, putting shapes together, etc. I also took a good look at the Dienes' MAB material. Some time before I had considered introducing structural material as an additional aid to affirm work which was going on in number from a variety of experiences. The Dienes' MAB seemed the most suitable for using the 'discovery approach' — children finding out for themselves — and to assist understanding of place value and operations in a logical way which children could see for themselves. At the same time I made a few assignments for older children on geometrical topics, and arranged the science so that with these children it had a 'mathematical' bias which led to recording in many cases in graphical form. We had also begun some discovery in science with the youngest children and some of this we found useful for emphasising that mathematics should not be considered in isolation. Television was used extensively in the school mainly as enrichment material to provide one more stimulus for creative expression. A series on primary mathematics was due to be broadcast and I decided to use this as additional background material and source of ideas. The series certainly provided ideas for us to develop in our own way, but otherwise was of little value.

So much for the material and ideas; now how was this put into practice? Due to a drop in the school roll we had an empty room and this soon became full of apparatus and equipment for mathematics and science, some bought, much acquired as 'odds and ends'. This room also housed the television receiver, and was used by small groups of children at various times for many other activities such as needlework, art, craft, music, sometimes supervised, at other times working on their own. At first, with the classes in some cases as large as forty-seven, I felt that I must help the teachers, and as I wanted to make the main impact with the youngest children the spare room was used a great deal with them. I would take half the first-year junior class each day in this room and the class teacher would take the remainder in her own classroom. But, of course, this did not necessarily mean that the children remained in the rooms all the time. Much activity took place in the corridors, the hall and outside in the playground. For each group the time each week was roughly divided into two, half being spent in 'number' work using materials such as Dienes' MAB, and half with 'practical' work from the assignment sheets I had prepared which involved weights and measures, time, spatial activities and so on. This was a mixed ability class and it soon became apparent that about half the class really needed other number activities using such things as number strips, ladders, squares, etc., before they used the Dienes material. What computation was done arose mainly from the practical work, and no 'sums' as such were done. With the other classes I would take either the whole class, or a group of children, about twice a week. The second-year children used some of the more difficult assignments from the first year, and the older children in the third and fourth years used more assignments I contrived which were largely concerned with shape and size, and also

some associated with their work in science. In all cases the class teachers would continue with this work in their own time, and they began to devise some of their own ideas from my basic suggestions, and by using some of the newer books as sources of ideas. This work and organisation continued the following year with modifications which arose from our experiences in the first year. Many of the assignments had to be revised for both mathematical ideas and the vocabulary used. The original thirty-six became fifty or so, others were added in the upper part of the school, and the climate of discovery and questioning on the part of the children, already evident in other activities, led to some mathematics arising incidentally from other sources. To make a rough assessment of the level of 'mathematical readiness' of the young children coming from the infant school I spent about a fortnight at the beginning of this school year giving each child an individual test. I sat down with each in my room, or some other quiet spot, and presented situations in a 'practical' way — not a written test to be answered on paper. These involved such things as conservation of quantity, counting and recognising patterns (seeing whether the children used 'counting-on' or not), enumeration and knowledge of numerals, the ability to group objects and count in such situations, the ability to share (and cope if any objects were left over), the notion of ordinal number and the appreciation of quantitative order. From these tests it was possible to put the children into workable groups for number activities. Some appeared ready to use the Dienes' MAB, many required other activities with number strips, collections of objects for grouping and counting, finding patterns on number squares, ladders and strips for introducing ordinal number, and so on. In the practical discovery work on weights, measures, money, time, shapes, etc., some children required activities of an easier nature than those on the original set of work cards, and in these cases the instructions frequently were given orally by the teacher to a small group of children working together. In this second stage of the development of the work throughout the school a much bigger effort was also made with the older children. Many more 'assignments' were given to these children based on ideas similar to those suggested by H.M.I. Miss Biggs on her courses, and others associated with work in activities such as science and geography. From these a large amount of graphical representation developed. Number work was extended through investigation of patterns, and *occasionally* use was made of Dienes' Algebraic Experience Material for a specific purpose, such as finding out about prime numbers, square numbers, the commutative principle, the associative principle, and so on, all this being done through personal discovery. This latter material was useful as a time-saver at that stage of development as the preparation of materials can occupy a great deal of time, and one has to be sensible about allocating time to the best advantage of the school; but experience soon showed that the ideas might well have been discovered with 'home-made' material. Gradually, as the teachers became accustomed to working with the classes in groups, or even with the children at individual activities – and remember, this was not something entirely new to them, for it had been developed in other school work for some time – and as the ideas for activities built up, it became apparent that I could withdraw more and more from the classroom and become more useful as an adviser when teachers wanted more ideas for development of the work. The spare room became used less and less, except when small groups of children would go there on their own to work at a special interest, e.g. it was used for some time by a group of four second-year boys who were engaged on making a huge map of the district. In fact, this became so big that eventually they decided to go one step further and spread it out on the hall floor. And it is interesting to note that in my absence during this present year the teachers like working in their rooms rather than going to a special mathematics room.

Looking back over the last four or five years it is also noticeable that the schemes of work in mathematics have changed considerably. At the beginning of my time as headmaster the scheme I introduced was very much a syllabus outlining processes and techniques to be covered by each class each term. Now it has changed to a general outline of ideas and suggestions which has been a joint effort by me and the staff, developing in the light of experience of the ideas I wanted to introduce, and which they have carried out. From these joint efforts we have amended and revised this general scheme three times in the past three years. Its main purpose,

I suppose, is not so much to help established members of the staff, but newcomers. The scheme for the established teachers is in their minds from daily contact and discussion with me and among themselves. Newcomers are given the scheme to read over and get the basic ideas, and where possible are invited to spend a day or two with us, before they take up their appointments.

From a head teacher's point of view what has this experience of reorganising the mathematics in the school shown me? First, that one must be convinced that this is the right way to teach mathematics, and that teachers must teach from conviction, too; and the best way to convince staff (if there are any doubters) is by example, and not by throwing them in 'at the deep end' and leaving them to sink or swim.

Of course, the most frequent question from the doubters is, 'How will this affect the standards of computation?', meaning 'sums'. And this comes from parents, too, as I mention later. Mr. Boucher, in his article in Appendix I, has already given the answer to this in a manner which should satisfy any who may still have doubts, and perhaps I can best re-affirm what he says by giving some examples of what happened in my school. At the end of one year, for no other reason than just interest to see what would happen, I gave the first-year class a short 'sum' test in weights and measures, money, etc. These were children who had done some number work with strips, ladders, abaci, number squares, Dienes' MAB, and so on, but very little formal practice, and *none at all* in weights and measures and money. In the latter field the work has been entirely practical with recording their discoveries in various ways. But the majority had no difficulty in coping with 'sums' I set, provided these were within the range of their practical experience. Certainly some of the test 'sums' may have been a little easier than if the children had had lessons and lessons in nothing but computation practice. But it did show that far less practice was needed to enable the children to understand what they were doing when presented with 'sums'. The other two examples show how children tackled computation in new situations. Following some measuring activities a second-year boy (8+) was given as practice this: 423×36. He had never seen 'long

multiplication' before, nor been shown how to do it. But through his number work and experience he could cope with multiplying 'tens and units' by 6, and he also knew that the 3 in 36 represented 30. In fact, he was one of a group of children who, when adding such numbers as 36 and 47, would refer to the 'tens' not as 3 and 4, but 30 and 40. He attempted the long multiplication in this way:
on one part of a sheet of paper he wrote

$$423 \\ \times\ 6 \\ \overline{2538}$$

with appropriate 'carrying figures' where necessary. Down another part of the paper he wrote

$$4230 \\ 4230 \\ 4230 \\ \overline{12690}$$

his knowledge of place value from using Dienes' MAB enabling him to arrive at 423×10 as 4230. In a third, different, spot he put down

$$2538 \\ 12690 \\ \overline{15228}$$

He explained his method sensibly to his teacher and this gave her the opportunity to discuss with him a tidier, and more economical way, of setting out what, in fact, he had discovered for himself.

The second example concerns another second-year boy of about the same age. A group of children in this class, who had finished using the Dienes' MAB for some time, were presented with the following:

$$111 \\ +\ 101 \\ \overline{212}$$

When asked if this was correct one boy answered, 'Yes, if it is a sum in base 3, or any base bigger than 3'. The interesting thing to the teacher was that he did not answer just 'Yes', for she had expected this kind of reply, or laughter from the children that it was too easy. The boy had obviously thought about the problem more deeply. As an interesting sideline, the teacher developed the situation by asking what figures would be used if they were working in base 2 (which had not been considered before). There was no hesitation in giving the answer 0 and 1 — which, incidentally, they thought highly amusing. The group then did a few easy 'sums' in binary, for each other, for fun.

There must be a climate in the school which encourages freedom on the part of the children to work in groups anywhere about the school, and to talk with teachers when they feel it necessary rather than having to wait for the teacher to tell them something. We were fortunate in this respect, as this was nothing new. Children had been used to working in this way in other activities for some years; and teachers and children accepted without question such situations as a small group of children walking quietly into the hall to measure a wall, for instance, while another class might be there for dancing or physical education, neither group taking undue notice or interfering with the work of the other.

By taking such a large part myself at the beginning there was the disadvantage that the 'lessons' had to fit into a timetable to take into account my other commitments, whereas this approach to learning mathematics fits best into a less rigid arrangement. However, one has to weigh up the advantages and disadvantages, and at the time this seemed the best way to make a start. Perhaps I did make too big a start with one class, and looking back it may have been better to make the transition more slowly by having a few children from the class working at 'discovery' methods each day. In starting the way that I did I was influenced by the fact that I had sufficient apparatus and materials to make a fairly big start, but this will not be the case in many schools. If a small amount of equipment is acquired from time to time — and the cost influences this — then a small group of about eight to start with seems the best idea, gradually building up as more material and ideas become available.

Another factor in favour of starting slowly with a small group of children is the 'training' in this way of working for children who may not have encountered it before. This applies particularly to the use of 'assignment' cards, and finding the appropriate apparatus and material. Some four or five periods in the first two weeks of term were given to this. The teacher would explain the system of using the cards, and the children would practise moving about, obtaining apparatus, putting it away, and so on. This is essential if the teacher does not want chaos at the first attempt or to be surrounded by children clamouring to know where various pieces of apparatus are kept.

This question of a small beginning also came up when considering the problem of staff changes, and the arrival of teachers who might not be as convinced about the value of this way of teaching mathematics as those who had been with me from the beginning. And this did occasionally occur. In such cases, after a short settling-in period when the new teacher could begin to sense the atmosphere in the school, and during which he was allowed to proceed in his own way, I would suggest that he made a very small beginning by allowing a group of about eight children to work at 'discovery' methods, using cards and other ideas provided by me and other teachers, for one or two periods a week, and then later daily, so that he could see that 'it did work'. In this I was helped by two factors: the co-operation of the other teachers who soon made newcomers feel at home and indirectly saw that some of our ideas 'rubbed off' on them; and that a new teacher in most cases would be taking over a class which had been used to working in this way in any case. So the problem was not the children, but convincing the teacher, and as with everything this was best done by example.

It was also noticeable that nothing stands still. As the enthusiasm of the children and teachers increased so there was a gradual development of ideas introduced for activities, and in ways of organising the work in the classrooms and elsewhere. And at the present moment many of the ideas and assignments are unrecognisable when compared with those with which we started. There comes a time, too, which varies from person to person, when teachers feel the need for more mathematics for themselves, and they begin to enquire about courses and suitable books to read.

On the question of money, I saved by not buying arithmetic text books, and in addition we were allowed a small special allowance for science equipment. This was frequently used for materials and apparatus which could be used equally well for mathematics and science, and I was fortunate in occasionally receiving an increased allowance when other schools did not spend theirs. Ideally, of course, there should be sufficient material in each classroom for every child to have access to whatever he might need to tackle and solve a problem, but this takes a long time, and even in our case I would say that after five years we still had not reached this situation. But a slow beginning and a gradual build-up, co-operation between teachers, and between children within a class, about a sensible use of available material, allows the work to progress steadily. One further point on buying apparatus and equipment, and this was learnt from experience – or rather from mistakes: do, whenever possible, try to see the actual things before you order them, and consider carefully whether any piece is really going to be of use. Catalogues are certainly useful, but it is easy to get misled by pictures and descriptions. Equipment which I found needed special care in buying: much of that connected with activities on weight (suitable balances are not easy to obtain within the primary school price range, metal weights need looking at carefully, compression-type scales and extension-type spring balances must be considered carefully to see that they cover the range required for the assignments in mind); trundle wheels, which should be studied to see that the 'click' mechanism is robust enough to stand up to constant use; equalisers, which frequently do not balance satisfactorily – it may be advisable to make one's own; stop-watches which need not be expensive models when adequate ones can be obtained from suppliers of 'ex-Armed Forces equipment' at a considerable reduction in price. Representatives of firms will frequently put on local displays of equipment. Another way is to examine the apparatus used on teachers' courses, and I found that used by Miss Biggs particularly useful in helping me to assess the value and suitability of items to be used in school. Spending money wisely is an important part of the organisation of the work, and it is easy to obtain unsuitable equipment through not considering this aspect carefully enough.

The most gratifying aspect of the whole operation was the willingness on the part of the teachers to learn what to them might be 'new' mathematics, and this I think came from three things: they were always a forward-looking group of teachers willing to discuss and learn about new ideas; they had seen the impact of a similar approach in other school work over a period of years; and they felt that if I was prepared to devote so much time in the classroom to ease their burdens in the initial stages then it was worth having a go.

In all this one mustn't forget the part played by the local education authority in assisting the teachers through courses which affirmed their ideas, but more especially from the real encouragement and sincere interest shown in our work by the chief education officer himself, and by his advisory staff, all of whom went to great lengths to help us in whatever way they could.

And what about the children? The most noticeable effect was in the enjoyment of their mathematics. In the past we had occasionally had children who didn't want to come to school because they 'couldn't do sums', and this was accompanied by the inevitable tears. Perhaps the changed attitude can best be illustrated by recounting an actual incident — still accompanied by tears. Janet, who was just 8 years old, had a shocking cold one Monday morning and really should have stayed at home. She went home for her mid-day meal, and didn't appear in the afternoon. On the Tuesday morning her mother came to school to tell me the reason for Janet's absence, and in the course of the conversation said, 'I had a terrible time with Janet yesterday afternoon because I wouldn't let her come to school. She cried and cried because she wouldn't be able to do her maths'. What different tears!

One other thing has been evident. We have in the past underestimated what many of our children could do in mathematics through limiting them to the narrow field of 'sums'. By widening the scope of the mathematics our eyes have been opened to some of the things they can tackle and understand.

Finally, and probably most important, we come to the parents. Co-operation had always been excellent, and this was without an official parent-teacher body. But through various activities the parents had provided us indirectly with many library books, with a pottery kiln, a television receiver and a tape recorder. They had always been interested in new ideas, and meetings in the past on such things as the teaching of italic handwriting, reading and the use of books, techniques in arithmetic, had been well attended. Even so, I could see that there might be doubts and queries if children went home with stories that they were not doing 'sums'. So I got in first, and invited parents to come along one afternoon in September each year to hear what I intended to do. They saw the kind of practical activities that their children would be doing, looked at the structural apparatus, and heard something of the ideas behind this 'new' approach. On Open Days the apparatus, assignments, etc., were available for them to see and try if they felt like it, and in addition to the usual displays of art, needlework, etc., a large display of the children's mathematical work was mounted in the school hall. To reach parents of children who entered the school during the past two years, the most recent idea was to have the school open during the day for parents to come along and see the actual work in operation, and again to try some for themselves with their children.

What I have written is not meant as something for others to copy. Each school has its own problems, its own principles, and one cannot lay down a 'standard method'. Rather this article is an attempt to show how one school reorganised its mathematics and how initial problems were overcome. But I am sure that, given the conviction that something should be done, problems of organisation will soon disappear, and other schools will achieve far greater success than we did.

Appendix 3

Can the Colleges of Education help?
by J. Breakell, a lecturer at a College of Education

1   Teacher-training in college

Students, on arrival in college, tend to be very conservative in their attitude to mathematics. Many will have an 'O' level qualification in the subject, but it is demonstrable that the majority have little or no understanding of the mathematics which they had been called upon to do in their school days, and actively dislike the subject. They tend to be sceptical about a new approach to primary mathematics with its emphasis on 'discovery' work, and the majority still think of the work as consisting of graded exercises in the four rules of arithmetic.

The attitudes described above, which are largely a function of their own training, are difficult to break down. Some considerable time elapses before a typical student begins to think freely about the implications of what is offered to a primary school child and, of course, about the manner in which the material is presented.

It is essential that a student should be offered wide opportunities to participate in 'discovery' work at his own level, for only through this approach will he really understand the significance for children. It is also vitally important that he should be made aware of the psychological background to this approach, with particular reference to the work of Piaget, so that he may leave college equipped not only with the fundamental ideas for providing mathematical experiences for children, but also with an awareness of the significance of the stages of intellectual development through which a child passes in his primary years.

2   Meeting teachers in schools

Following the establishment of regular two-day in-service courses for teachers in the area, which were under my direction, I was asked to visit individual schools to talk to the staff, perhaps over tea, about the new approach to primary mathematics. Contacts of this sort were invariably made because one of the teachers on the staff had attended a two-day course. At first I gave a short outline talk for about twenty to thirty minutes and then the meeting was thrown open to discussion for a similar period. Although this arrangement, and particularly the exchange of ideas in the discussion time, was valuable, it soon became apparent that we were talking 'in vacuo' to a large extent. Consequently I decided to take along to these meetings a limited amount of materials and equipment and to allow teachers to experiment frequently, using assignments which had been found suitable for primary children. Nowadays, after listening to a short introductory statement which poses the problems inherent in reconsidering primary mathematics, teachers spend some thirty minutes (or longer if, as often happens, they are reluctant to finish) in working in this way. There follows a short talk, where an attempt is made to review the relevant work in the field of psychology concerning intellectual development and its special significance in connection with the 'discovery' approach. A general discussion ensues. As in work with children, the two most important factors in all this are discovery and discussion.

This work has its lighter moments, for on one occasion when I had taken some materials and equipment into a school at about 3.30 p.m., and had begun to set them out for the use of teachers, some 35 infants entered the hall. They were naturally extremely curious, and began to handle the various articles on show. This in itself was quite acceptable, but it gradually became borne in on me that the children were under the impression that my activities represented the opening stages of a jumble sale, and this was spectacularly confirmed when one little girl offered me $2\frac{1}{2}$d. for the remainder of the Jelly Babies which we happened to be using at that time.

3   Working with children

In order to apply practically some of the ideas which had been discussed in both college and school, as well as on the two-day courses, I made arrangements to visit schools with a view to testing children on the lines that Piaget has described, and also to introduce some mathematical assignments to children who had had little or no experience of the 'discovery' approach before. These arrangements were almost always made as a result of previous contacts — on two-day courses or at the evening meetings with teachers.

a Testing The carrying out of the Piagetian tests with primary children of different ages never fails to produce some surprises. Although a visitor may be mildly astonished when the tests produce results which do not accord with the apparent intellectual attainment of a particular child, the class teacher is often frankly amazed, for example as when the child clearly shows that he lacks the true concept of length, volume, or the conservation of a number quantity.

This kind of testing occasionally produces some amusing incidents. On one occasion I was carefully questioning a boy of seven about the conservation of the volume of a liquid, which involves comparison of heights of the liquid in vessels of different diameter. Undoubtedly the boy was within an ace of understanding conservation and for this reason I expect the questioning was somewhat repetitive and went on for a longer period than usual. When I had left, the boy asked his teacher why I had been asking all the questions about the liquid in the vessel, and couldn't I see very well?

b Introducing discovery work When a visitor enters a classroom, even comparatively regularly, for the purpose of introducing some discovery work, the situation is largely artificial, and any project of this type must be carried on within the limitations of this proviso. In the school about which I am thinking, the class concerned consisted of forty children aged about ten. I took along the necessary equipment and materials for some forty experiments, together with assignment cards. The furniture in the room, which had been arranged formally, was quickly reorganised to form several working surfaces, making use of spare blackboards, and the equipment and assignment cards were laid out. The children were encouraged to work in pairs and to select their own assignments.

Since the children had not been used to working in this way,

it is true that the noise level was high for some twenty minutes, but eventually declined to an acceptable level as the children became absorbed. It is true also that the children wanted a great deal of direction at first, but once again they gradually learned to think first and take their own decisions. Quite quickly it was possible to circulate in the room, and to discuss a particular problem with a pair of children, make a suggestion, or put a further question. For the most part, even on the first occasion, the children were gainfully employed on their experiments. They were interested and therefore absorbed.

On one occasion I took a spot check and estimated that thirty-five of the forty children were profitably employed. Of the five who were not, it appeared on enquiry that for two of the children the language on the assignment card was too difficult, and therefore it failed to communicate the essence of the problem. Whether the problem itself was too difficult I could not determine at that time. In another case, that of a child who was highly intelligent, I must presume that he was not being sufficiently stretched by anything that he was offered.

A great deal of emphasis was placed on the recording of findings in graphical form and a use to which a completed graph may be put, that is to say, interpolation. The development of this side of the work from the more elementary block graph onwards took considerable time, as did of course the meaningful use of the technique of interpolation.

At first the children, though absorbed, tended to rush through the mechanics of one assignment, ignoring the underlying mathematical implications, and to hasten on to another. This is a factor which must be guarded against, particularly when transferring from the passive system of 'being taught' arithmetic to the more active approach being discussed here. The teacher must exercise patience in many ways in beginning this work to ensure that the children have the opportunity of understanding the mathematical significance of an experiment. This can only be achieved through discussion with them, and in allowing children to find out for themselves — being an adviser rather than a 'teacher'.

4 Meeting parents

In schools where new methods of learning mathematics are being introduced it is quite easy for parents to become anxious about their children's activities. Children might tell their parents, particularly if they have been extremely interested in their tasks, that they have been, say, weighing sand against beans, or running a toy car down a slope that day.

It is obviously tremendously important that parents should be fully aware of the implications of this new approach to the learning of mathematics at the primary stage, particularly when, almost inevitably, their standard measurement will be the traditional one of how many sums have been done that day.

Several head teachers who have been concerned about this problem asked me to talk to their parent–teacher organisations, or in certain cases to a specially-called meeting. Although at first the evening's activities were confined to a talk followed by questions, the same limitations as were obvious in the meetings of teachers' groups became apparent. To a large extent there was little of a concrete nature on which to base our discussions.

Consequently I began to take a limited amount of material and equipment along to these meetings, together with assignment sheets, and after a short introductory statement outlining the characteristics of contemporary problems related to primary mathematics, parents were encouraged to spend thirty to forty minutes trying some of the experiments for themselves, recording their results graphically if appropriate.

When the audience resumed their seats (and this, too, was often delayed since parents became extremely absorbed in the experiments), I attempted to summarise our main aims in fostering the 'discovery' approach in mathematics, making passing reference to the work of the developmental psychologists and their importance to our work in this field. There followed a question and answer session, which, depending on the type of audience, could be on the one hand largely concerned with questions on the value of learning the multiplication tables, or on the other hand could be concerned with the implications of this approach to the learning of mathematics within the framework of modern educational practice with its emphasis on creativity.

Parents, particularly of able children, need reassurance that the skills necessary to pass a formal examination will be acquired in the course of this new kind of work. What is not so easy to demonstrate is that the foundations of mathematical thinking and understanding (which in the long run are much more important) are laid in children's experiences. Nevertheless, I feel once these reassurances with regard to formal skills have been given, parents will readily take on trust the value that accrues when children learn through their own discoveries.

5 Summary and conclusion

The activities described above have, I feel, helped to encourage the hesitant teacher to launch into this kind of mathematical activity. An attempt has been made to influence the climate of opinion so that students who have become aware of these developments at college may have increased opportunity on teaching practice to experiment with 'discovery' methods in primary mathematics under the supervision of teachers who are already acquainted with the basic tenets of this approach.

When I have been working with a class of children in school the head teacher has invariably made arrangements for all his staff to visit the room for some period of time. This has often provoked useful discussion in the staff room afterwards.

Sometimes a head teacher, when thinking of introducing a new approach to primary mathematics, will call a meeting of parents first to explain the proposed scheme. In my experience this has never been as satisfactory as the calling of a parents' meeting once the work is under way.

Some of the simple Piagetian tests can be extremely useful to a teacher in attempting to estimate a child's level of intellectual maturation. Frequently when I have undertaken such tests, a teacher has become aware of the nature of the child's difficulty for the first time, and is consequently the more able to provide activities suitable for the child's particular needs.

Within the framework of this appendix I have tried to stress the vital importance of contact between teachers and parents and between teachers and training college lecturers. Links established amongst students, teachers, parents and lecturers will promote a fuller understanding of what we are all trying to achieve both in the immediate field of 'discovery' mathematics and in the wider field of education as a whole.

Consultative committee

Chairman | Professor W H Cockcroft
J W G Boucher
R C Lyness
Miss B M Mogford (1964-1966)
H S Mullaly (from 1966)
R Openshaw
N Payne (from 1967)
D R F Roseveare
J Shanks (from 1966)
A G Sillitto (died 1966)
P F Surman
Dr D R Taunt
Mrs D E Whittaker (from 1967)
F Woolaghan
Professor J Wrigley

Organiser
Dr Geoffrey Matthews

Team members

1965 – 1966
J W G Boucher
G B Corston
H Fletcher
Miss B A Jackson
D E Mansfield
Miss B M Mogford

1966 – 1967
D R Brighton
Miss I Campbell
H Fletcher
D E Mansfield
J H D Parker
Miss R K Tobias
A G Vosper

1967 – 1968
E A Albany
D R Brighton
Miss I Campbell
Miss R K Tobias
A G Vosper

Designer
Ivan Dodd